Illustrated
MOSS FLORA
OF
FENNOSCANDIA

Edited by THE BOTANICAL SOCIETY OF LUND

II. *Musci*

By ELSA NYHOLM

FASC. I

CWK GLEERUP / LUND SWEDEN / 1954

NYA LITOGRAFEN
MALMÖ 1954
7709

INNEHÅLL

4

Order 3. **Pottiales**

PREFACE

The need for a practical illustrated flora of the Scandinavian mosses has been felt for a long time. Workers in all fields of botany, forestry, limnology, etc. in whose investigations mosses may be of great importance, have often been obliged to devote much time and work to even the simplest moss identification. It has been difficult, or almost impossible, for a beginner to penetrate into the moss taxonomy of the older Scandinavian floras.

In order to remedy this situation I began to make drawings of mosses, with the idea of publishing an illustrated edition of C. Jensen's "Skandinavisk Bladmossflora". Soon, however, I realized that much in that flora was out of date and in need of revision. For this reason I decided to publish an entirely new moss flora.

The drawings, illustrating each species mentioned in the text, are the work of the author; as far as possible, Scandinavian material has been used for this purpose, and any departure from this rule is specially noted.

Regarding taxonomy, I have, in accordance with V. F. Brotherus in his revision of the mosses in A. Engler, "Die natürlichen Pflanzenfamilien" and in "Die Laubmoose Fennoskandias", in the main, followed Max Fleischer.

The nomenclature follows "An Annotated List of British Mosses" (Trans. Brit. Bryol. Soc., vol. 1, 1950). In a few cases alterations have been made, mostly after having conferred with Mr. Olle Mårtensson, Fil. Lic., Uppsala.

The taxonomic value of the many forms and varieties of moss species is, in many cases, very uncertain. Some of these mentioned in our floras probably represent habitat modification, but in order to differentiate between this and genuine genotypic variation, cultivation experiments are necessary. I have, however, retained a number of the forms and varieties in this work, despite the fact that the majority of them may ultimately prove to be of little value.

The first part of the work comprises the families Fissidentaceae, Archidiaceae, Ditrichaceae, Seligeriaceae, Dicranaceae, and Encalyptaceae. The second part will, it is hoped, be completed within a year and is planned to include the families up to Bryaceae.

In the course of the work I have had the privilege of corresponding with a number of bryologists. First I wish to mention Dr. Herman Persson, Stockholm, who has shown a never-failing interest in my work, and Mr. Olle Mårtensson, Fil. Lic., Uppsala, with whom I have discussed questions of nomenclature as well as problems of species and variation. — Prof. R. Tuomikoski, Helsingfors, has offered valuable advice and has made suggestions concerning several critical genera and species. — The eminent Fissidens specialist M.

Potier de la Varde has assisted in the determination and identification of two Fissidens species. — I have received further help and support from the following bryologists: — Dr. N. Albertsson, Uppsala; A. C. Crundwell, Ph. D., Glasgow; Dr. O. Gjaerevoll, Trondheim; Mr. K. Holmen, Cand. Mag., Lyngby; Mr. Å. Hovgard, Governor of Gotland; Dr. E. von Krusenstjerna, Djursholm; Dr. P. A. Larsson, Öjersbyn; Mr. P. O. Nyman, Fil. Kand., Uppsala; Mr. Å. Persson, Fil. Mag., Lund; Mr. B. Pettersson, Fil. Lic., Uppsala; Prof. H. Reimers, Berlin; Dr. H. Sjörs, Lund; Mr. G. Skovgaard Christensen, Söborg; Mr. W. R. Uggla, Colonel, Stockholm; and Dr. S. Waldheim, Lund.

From a linguistic point of view the book has been critically and carefully read by an English bryologist, Miss Elizabeth Evans, Ph. D., of the Nature Conservancy.

The work could never have been carried out without the financial aid granted by Lars Hiertas Minne, the Hierta-Retzius foundation, and Statens Naturvetenskapliga Forskningsråd. To the boards of the said foundations and to Statens Naturvetenskapliga Forskningsråd I express my great indebtedness and gratitude.

To my chief at the Botanical Museum at Lund, Prof. H. Weimarck, I wish to express my deep-felt gratitude for the support he has given me in my work.

I also tender my sincere thanks to all who have otherwise assisted me and shown interest in my work.

Lund, April 1954.

Elsa Tufvesson-Nyholm.

Definition of terms

Acrocarpous, fruit terminal on stem or branch. (Fig. 1).

Acuminate, gradually tapering to a point.

Acute, terminating at once in a sharp point.

Alar or *angular cells*, cells at the basal angle of the leaf.

Amphithecium, the outer layers of cells of the sporogonium.

Androecium, ♂ inflorescence.

Angular cells. See *Alar cells.*

Annulus, a ring of specialized cells between the lid and the mouth of the capsule. These cells are often vesicular and highly elastic. (Fig. 17 a).

Antheridium, ♂ reproductive organ containing the antherozoides.

Apical, belonging to the apex or point.

Apiculus, a short, abrupt point continued from the lamina.

Apiculate, ending in an apiculus.

Apophysis. See *Hypophysis.*

Appendiculate cilia, cilia with short transverse bars at intervals.

Appressed, in erect position, applied closely to the stem.

Archegonium, ♀ reproductive organ.

Arcuate, bent in a curve like a bow.

Areolation, the network formed by the cells.

Aristate, ending in a fine bristly point.

Auricle, the small lobe or special patch of cells at the basal angle of a leaf.

Auriculate, having auricles.

Autoicous, having ♂ and ♀ organs on the same plant but in separate inflorescences.

Axil, the upper angle or hollow at the base of a leaf or branch, between it and the stem.

Axillary, belonging to, or in an axil.

Bicostate, having a double costa.

Bistratose, of two layers of cells.

Bordered, having a margin different from the rest of the leaf. (Fig. 2).

Bracts, the leaves enclosing the reproductive organs.

Caespitose, tufted.

Calyptra, the membranous veil or hood covering the lid. (Fig. 3).

Campanulate, bell-shaped.

Canaliculate, channelled.

Capillary, hair-like.

Carinate, keeled like a boat.

Central strand, a bundle of narrow and slender cells in the middle of many moss stems. (Fig. 4 c).

Cernuous, slightly drooping. (Fig. 5 a). See *pendulous.*

Cilia, hair-like threads.

Ciliate, with cilia.

Circinate, curved into a circle.

Cirrate, curled.

Cladocarpous, having the sporophyte terminating a short, special, fertile branch. (Fig. 6).

Cleistocarpous, capsule opening irregularly, not by means of lid.

Cochleariform, rounded and concave, like a spoon.
Collenchymatous, (of cells) having the walls thickened at the angles.
Collum, the neck or tapering base of the capsule.
Columella, the central column of the capsule. (Fig. 7).
Complanate, flattened.
Convolute, rolled together.
Cortical, belonging to the bark or cortex.
Costa, nerve or midrib of a moss leaf.
Crenate, having fine convex or rounded teeth.
Crenulate, minutely crenate.
Crisped, curled and twisted.
Cryptopore (stoma), immersed. (Fig. 8 a). See *phaneropore*.
Cucullate, hood-shaped and (of the calyptra) split on one side only. (Fig. 9 and 3 b).
Cuspidate, having a moderately long, stiff, acute point. (Fig. 10 a). See *mucronate*.
Cuticle, the outermost skin of epidermis cells.
Cygneous, curved like a swans neck. (Fig. 11).
Deciduous, falling off, not persistent.
Decurrent, with the base of the leaf running down the stem like wings.
Dendroid, tree-like.
Dentate, toothed.
Denticulate, minutely toothed.
Diminiate, split on one side.
Dioicous, ♂ and ♀ inflorescence on separate plants.
Distichous, in two opposite rows.
Dorsal, belonging to or on the back.
Emarginate, notched at end.
Emergent, half uncovered. See *exserted, immersed*.
Endemic, confined to a small geographical area.
Endostome, the internal peristome, see under *peristome*.
Endothecium, the inner layer of cells of the capsule.
Epiphragm, a membrane covering the mouth of the capsule.
Erecto-patent, midway between erect and patent.
Erose, irregularly notched as if gnawed.
Excurrent, projecting beyond the lamina.
Exostome, the exterior peristome. See under *peristome*.
Exothecial, belonging to the exothecium.
Exothecium, the outer membrane of the capsule.
Exserted, uncovered. See *emergent, immersed*.
Falcate, curved like a sickle.
Filiform, thread-like.
Fimbriate, fringed with cilia.
Flagella, very fine, string-like branches; e. g., *Dicranum flagellare*.
Flexuose, bent backward and forward, or wavy.
Gametophyte, the part of the plant which bears the sexual cells.
Gemma, a small, bud-like body capable of reproducing the plant.
Gemmiform, bud-like.
Gibbous, swollen on one side. (Fig. 12).
Glabrous, free from hair, smooth.
Glaucous, covered with bluish white bloom.
Globose, round like a ball.
Gregarious, growing near together but not in tufts.
Guide cells, the large leading cells seen in cross section of the nerve of some mosses. (Fig. 4 a). See *stereids*.
Gynoecium, the ♀ inflorescence.
Habit, the general form and aspect of a plant.
Habitat, the particular situation in which a plant grows.
Heteroicous, with more than one form of inflorescence in the same species (☿ + ♂ or ☿ + ♂ + ♀).
Heteromorphous, of different forms.

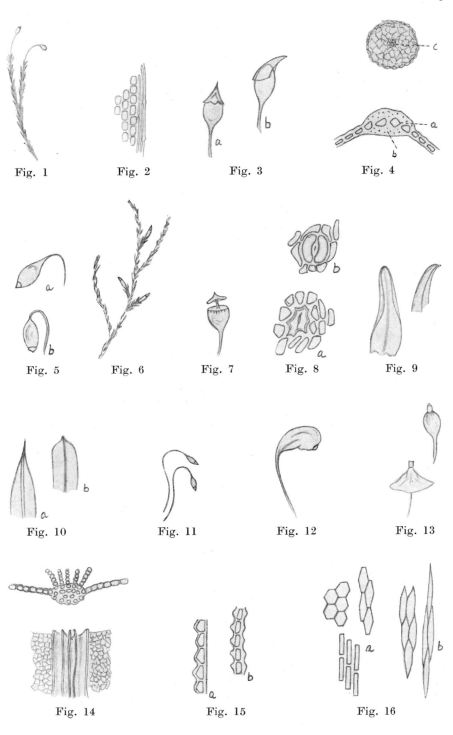

Fig. 1   Fig. 2   Fig. 3   Fig. 4

Fig. 5   Fig. 6   Fig. 7   Fig. 8   Fig. 9

Fig. 10   Fig. 11   Fig. 12   Fig. 13

Fig. 14   Fig. 15   Fig. 16

Hypophysis, a swelling round the base of the capsule. (Fig. 13).

Hyaline, colourless, without chlorophyll.

Imbricate, closely overlapping like tiles.

Immersed, covered by surrounding parts. See *emergent, exserted.*

Incrassate, of the cells, having thickened walls; of the cell-walls, thickened.

Inflorescence, often applied to the clusters of reproductive organs.

Insertion, the line of juncture of a leaf with the stem.

Involute, rolled inwards.

Involucre, whorl of bracts surrounding inflorescence.

Julaceous, smoothly cylindrical, worm-like.

Laciniate or *lacerate*, slashed, cut, irregularly torn.

Lamellae, sheets or plates of a tissue. (Fig. 14).

Lamina, the expanded part of a leaf excluding the nerve.

Lanceolate, shaped like a lance.

Lateral, belonging to the side.

Ligulate, strap-shaped, — longer and narrower than lingulate.

Linear, narrow, with the margins parallel.

Lingulate, tongue-shaped.

Lumen, the cavity or space within a cell.

Mamillae, small prominences on unthickened cell walls. (Fig. 15 a). See *papillae.*

Marginal, at the edge.

Mitriform, hood-shaped, symmetrical, cleft on two or more sides. (Fig. 3 a). See *cucullate.*

Monoicous, ♂ and ♀ organs on the same plant.

Mucro, a short, abrupt point formed by the excurrent nerve.

Mucronate, having a mucro. (Fig. 10 b). See *cuspidate.*

Muricate, *muriculate* (spore), rough with minute, sharp points.

Neck, the tapering base of the capsule. See also *collum.*

Nodose, knobbed.

Nodulose, with small knobs.

Oblong, with one axis longer than the other.

Obovate, inversely egg-shaped, i.e., with the broadest part above.

Obtuse, terminating in a rounded end.

Ochrea, a thin sheath round the seta, terminating the vaginula.

Ovoid, egg-shaped.

Papillae, small prominences, formed by thickening of the cell walls. (Fig. 15 b). See *mamillae.*

Paraphyllia, minute, leaf-like, branched organs among the leaves.

Paraphyses, jointed hyaline hairs mixed with the reproductive organs.

Parenchymatous cells, cells with broad, transverse ends. (Fig. 16 a). See *prosenchymatous.*

Paroicous, ♂ and ♀ on the same shoot but not mixed together, naked antheridia occurring in axils of stem leaves below the archegonia.

Patent, spreading at an angle of 45° or more.

Patulous, more widely spreading than patent.

Pellucid, translucent but not hyaline.

Pendulous, hanging or drooping; more than in *cernuous*. (Fig. 5 b). See *cernuous.*

Percurrent, reaching to the point but not beyond.

Perichaetium, the involucre of a ☿ or ♀ inflorescence.

Perichaetial leaves or bracts, leaves surrounding ♀ reproductive organs.

Perigonium, the involucre of the ♂ inflorescence.

Perigonial leaves or bracts, leaves surrounding ♂ reproductive organs.

Peristome, the fringe surrounding the mouth of the capsule, upon removing the lid. This fringe may consist of a single or double row of *teeth*. The outer row is often spoken of as the *exostome*, the inner as the *endostome*. (Fig. 17).

Persistent, not falling off. See *deciduous.*

Phaneropore (stoma), superficial. (Fig. 8 b). See *cryptopore.*

Piliferous, ending in a fine hair point.

Pleurocarpous, fruit lateral from the stem or branch. (Fig. 18).

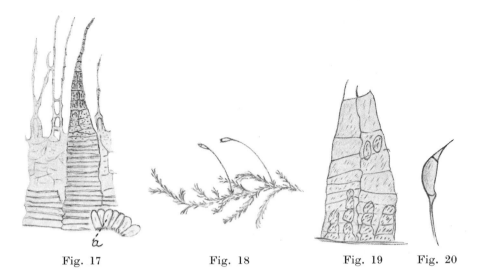

Fig. 17   Fig. 18   Fig. 19   Fig. 20

Plicate, folded in pleats or furrows.
Polymorphous, of many forms.
Polyoicous, the same species autoicous or dioicous.
Porose, perforated by pores.
Preperistome, see *prostome*.
Prosenchymatous, cells with pointed ends. (Fig. 16 b). See *parenchymatous*.
Prostome, thickening on the outer layer of the peristome. (Fig. 19).
Protonema, branched filiform threads produced by germinating spores.
Pseudoparaphyllia, rudimentary leaves, sometimes occurring at the juncture of
    a branch with the stem.
Pseudopodium, a leafless branch resembling a seta, but formed by the gameto-
    phyte, often bearing gemmae, e. g. *Aulacomnium androgynum*. In *Sphagnum*,
    the stalk (false seta) bearing the capsule.
Radicles, root-like filaments formed by the stem.
Radiculose, covered with radicles.
Recurved, curved back.
Reflexed, bent abruptly backwards.
Revolute, rolled back.
Rhizoid. See *radicles*.
Rhizome, a subterranean root-like stem, growing horizontally.
Rostellate, with a short beak.
Rostrate, with a long beak.
Rugose, wrinkled.
Scabrous, rough or warted.
Secund, turned to one side.
Serrate, with saw-like denticulations.
Serrulate, finely serrate.
Seta, stalk bearing the capsule, formed by the sporophyte.
Setaceous, bristle-like.
Sinuose, undulate, wavy.
Spatulate, from a narrower base gradually obovate.
Spinose, with sharp teeth.
Spinulose, with small sharp teeth.
Sporangium, the inner sac of the capsule, containing the spores.
Sporogonium, the capsule.

Squarrose, spreading out at right angles from the stem.
Stegocarpous, the capsule opening by a lid.
Stellate, arranged like a star, radiating from a centre.
Stereids, narrow cells with strongly incrassate walls, forming the strengthening tissue of leaves and stems. (Fig. 4 b).
Stoloniferous stem, a slender creeping stem with minute leaves.
Stomata, air pores in the epidermis.
Striate, having striae.
Struma, a swelling on one side at base of capsule. (Fig. 20).
Subula, a very fine, needle-like point.
Subulate, having a subula.
Sulcate, deeply furrowed.
Synoicous, ♂ and ♀ organs mixed in the same inflorescence, ☿.
Terminal, at the apex.
Tomentose, covered with woolly fibrils or a thick felt of radicles.
Turgid, swollen.
Utricle, somewhat inflated oblong cell in Sphagna.
Vaginant, sheathing.
Vaginula, the sheath round the base of the seta.
Ventral, in front, i. e. leaf-surface facing the stem.
Vermicular, narrow, cylindrical, and curved, like a worm.
Vesicular, inflated like a bladder.

Key to the figures

The figures of each species are drawn according to the following plan: First, at the left, there is a figure showing the habit of the plant (about life size), then two (or three) stem leaves, one from the lower part of the stem, the other from the upper part, further sometimes perichaetial (p) and perigonial leaves (pg); next is shown the capsule, sometimes with spores, peristome and cells of annulus. A figure showing the habit of a plant (enlarged) is occasionally last in the series.

The following signs are used throughout the figures:

ge Gemmae.
p   Perichaetial leaf.
pg Perigonial leaf.
pr Paraphyllia.
sp Spores.
x   Section; xl, cross section of a leaf; xm, cross section of a leaf margin; xn, cross section of a nerve; xs, cross section of a stem etc.

BRYALES

Capsule with or without seta, with lid and peristome or dehiscing irregularly. Spore-sac separated from the capsule wall by an air cavity. Spores developed from the endothecium. Columella reaching the top of the capsule.

Group 1. EUBRYALES

Peristome formed by membrane plates and derived from 2—3 concentric series of cells of the sporogonium. The exostome and endostome from the same layer of tissue.

Order 1. Fissidentales

The terminal cell of the stem bilateral. Leaves distichous in a single plane. Peristome single, teeth 16. Acrocarpous or pleurocarpous.

Fam. I. Fissidentaceae

Autoicous, dioicous or polyoicous, acrocarpous or pleurocarpous, when dioicous often with dwarf male plants. Leaves distichous in a single plane, half-clasping the stem. The leaf usually consists of three different parts: the sheathing lamina or the boat-formed part, the apical lamina, and the dorsal lamina. It is now generally accepted that the boat-formed part represents the original leaf; the remaining parts consist of two lamellae, one terminal (the apical lamina) and one dorsal (the dorsal lamina). In the dwar fmale plants these lamellae are absent and in the lower stem leaves they are often not or only slightly developed. The perichaetial leaves are like the stem leaves. The cells in the upper part of the leaf are more or less irregularly hexagonal, the basal cells are somewhat enlarged and more lengthened, leaf-margins with or without a border of narrow, elongated, colourless cells. Nerve (when developed) fairly strong, ending below the apex or percurrent, sometimes excurrent in a short point; in cross section with two stereid bands and one or two rows of guide cells. Capsule smooth, erect or cernuous, symmetrical or asymmetrical; peristome single, rarely rudimentary, red or brownish, in structure resembling that of *Dicranum*, — teeth divided to the middle, rarely entire, usually more or less distinctly vertically point-striated below, papillose above, sometimes spirally thickened, — when moist, teeth often bent into the capsule and closely pressed against the inside. Lid conical, longly or shortly rostellate. Calyptra small, conical, entire at base, mitriform or cucullate. Spores papillose or nearly smooth.

This family, with its typical leaf-form, is one of the most well-defined among the mosses. It has an almost global distribution from the arctic regions to the tropics; in the tropical region, however, is found the greatest number of species and forms. Except for a few small genera, *Fissidentaceae* consists of the genus *Fissidens* with about 1,000 species.

I   The apical lamina as long as the boat-formed part or
    somewhat longer or shorter; seta considerably longer
    than the perichaetial leaves .... 1. *Fissidens*
II The apical lamina 2—3 times as long as the boat-for-
    med part; seta short and thick, shorter or slightly
    longer than the perichaetial leaves .... 2. *Octodiceras*

1. Fissidens Hedw., Sp. Musc., 1801.

Usually autoicous or dioicous. Leaves mostly with two well developed lamellae, the apical shorter or slightly longer than the boat-formed part. Seta much longer than the perichaetial leaves, terminal or lateral; capsule with stomata, erect or curved; peristome divided approximately to the middle, below pointstriated, above papillose, ± striated.

I   Leaves with border of narrow cells; seta terminal
    1 Border strong, two or several cells thick, yellow or
      brownish
      a The apical lamina considerably shorter than the
        boat-formed part .... 2. *F. mildeanus*
      aa The apical lamina at least as long as the boat-
        formed part .... 1. *F. crassipes*
    2 Border one cell thick
      a Dorsal lamina of the upper leaves not reaching
        the stem, upper leaf cells 5—7 μ wide .... 3. *F. bambergeri*
      aa Dorsal lamina of the upper leaves reaching the
        stem, upper leaf cells 8—18 μ wide
        b Autoicous; budlike androecia or naked anthe-
          ridia in the axils of the leaves below the gyno-
          ecium .... 4. *F. bryoides*
        bb Dioicous; mostly with dwarf male plants in
          the radicles of the ♀ plants
          c Shoots with several leaves; on soil
            d Capsule erect
              e Nerve and border of the upper leaves ending
                in or just below the apex .... 5. *F. viridulus*
              ee Nerve and border of the upper leaves en-
                ding far below the apex .... 6. *F. haraldi*
            dd Capsule curved, horizontal or cernuous .... 7. *F. incurvus*
          cc Shoots with few leaves; on stones or rocks,
            usually aquatic
            d Leaves lanceolate, obtuse or acuminate; on
              siliceous boulders .... 8. *F. pusillus*
            dd Leaves narrow, gradually tapering to an
              acute point; on calcareous boulders .... 9. *F. minutulus*
II Leaves without border of narrow cells; seta terminal
    or lateral
    1 Sporogonium terminal
      a Minute, 1—2 mm high, stem with few pairs of
        leaves .... 10. *F. exilis*
      aa Tall, 1—2 cm high, stem with several pairs of
        leaves .... 11. *F. osmundoides*

2 Sporogonium lateral
  a Upper part of the leaves irregularly serrate, usu-
    ally with paler marginal border
    b Cells in the upper part of the leaves 14—20 μ;
      marginal cells only slightly incrassate, ± pale;
      growing on wet or damp soil .... 14. *F. adianthoides*
    bb Cells in the upper part of the leaves 9—12 μ;
      marginal cells incrassate, usually distinctly
      pale; on rocks or drier soil .... 13. *F. cristatus*
  aa Leaves nearly entire or finely and evenly crenu-
    late all round
    b Leaves broadly lanceolate; on soil .... 12. *F. taxifolius*
    bb Leaves narrowly and longly lanceolate; gro-
      wing in or close to water .... 15. *F. polyphyllus*

Sect. I. **Pachylomidium**: Leaves with a strong, coloured border of narrow, linear cells. Sporophyte terminal. Peristome teeth spirally thickened and papillose above. ± tall plants on stones in streams in calcareous districts.

1.   **F. crassipes** Wils., Msc. in Br. Eur., 1849; (*F. incurvus* β *fontanus* Br. Eur., 1843). — Fig. 1 A.
Autoicous or dioicous. Leaves narrowly lanceolate, the apical lamina usually longer than the boat-formed part, the dorsal lamina not reaching the base of the leaf; nerve brownish, ending close below the apex; cells in the upper part of the leaf thin-walled, 12—18 μ. Capsule erect, symmetrical, on a reddish seta, terminal. Spores 14—21 μ, finely papillose, mature in autumn. — Tufts dark green, 1—2 cm high on wet rocks, on submerged stones in streams, etc.

Only few localities. **F.** *Ta.* (South, Central and West Europe, Madeira, Algeria, Morocco, Asia Minor).

2.   **F. mildeanus** Schimp., Milde in Bot. Zeit., 1862; (*F. crassipes* β *rufipes* Schimp., Syn. Musc. Eur., 1876; *F. fontanus* Mitt. in Journ. Linn. Soc. Bot., 1885). — Fig. 1 B.
Autoicous or synoicous. Leaves lanceolate, sharply pointed, the apical lamina shorter than the boat-formed part, the basal lamina narrowed below, with a margin about 2 cells wide reaching the base of the leaf; nerve strong, becoming red-brown when old, ending below the apex; cells in the upper part of the leaf 11—14(—18) μ. Capsule erect or slightly inclined, symmetrical or somewhat asymmetrical, Spores 19—22 μ, nearly smooth, mature in winter. — Tufts green or brownish, 2—3 cm high, on calcareous rocks in streams.
Recorded from one locality in Scandinavia; but I have not seen specimens. **N.** *VFld.* (Central Europe).

Sect. II. **Bryoidium**: Leaves with a distinct border of narrow, linear, colourless cells. Sporophyte terminal. Peristome teeth spirally thickened and papillose above. Small plants on soil or *F. minutulus* and *F. pusillus* on stones.

3.   **F. bambergeri** Schimp., Milde in Bot. Zeit., 1864; (*F. viridulus* subsp. *Bambergeri* Waldh. in Jens., Skand. Bladmossfl., 1939). — Fig. 1 D.
Polyoicous with terminal, synoicous inflorescences, in rare cases naked archegonia are found with antheridia in the axils of the upper stem leaves. Leaves lingulate — lanceolate with a short minutely toothed point, dorsal lamina not reaching the base of the leaf; border thin and occurs only in the upper leaves, in the boat-formed part becoming wider and running into the lamina; the dorsal lamina is usually not bordered; nerve red-yellow, ending below the apex; cells in the upper part of the leaf 5—7(—9) μ. Capsule erect, small, obovate, symmetrical, seta red-yellow. Spores

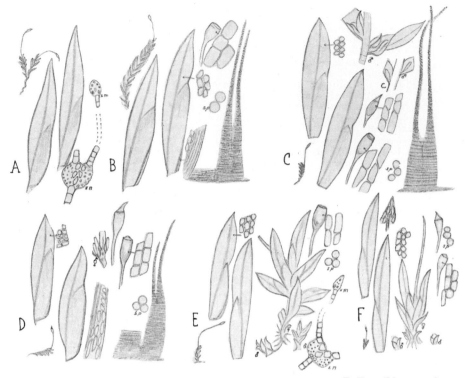

Fig. 1 A *Fissidens crassipes*, from spec. of Central Europe, B *F. mildeanus*, from spec. of Central Europe, C *F. bryoides*, c var. *gymnandrus*, D *F. bambergeri*, from spec. of Austria, Meran, E *F. viridulus*, F *F. minutulus*.

12—14 μ, very finely papillose, mature in winter. — In low, trailing mats on warm slopes.

Recorded from **N.** *Akh.* However, the specimens I have seen from this locality have been *F. bryoides.* (Central Europe, Azores, Egypt, North America).

This species is characterized by the synoicous, terminal inflorescences, the basal lamellae which do not reach the base of the leaf, and above all the small leaf cells. The plants are smaller than those of *F. bryoides* and *F. viridulus.*

4. F. bryoides Hedw., Sp. Musc., 1801. — Fig. 1 C.

Autoicous. Androecia bud-shaped in the axils of the leaves below the gynoecium. Leaves lingulate-lanceolate, shortly acuminate, the dorsal lamina reaching the base of the leaf; border mostly colourless, strong, at apex usually confluent with the nerve; nerve excurrent or percurrent, rarely ending below the apex; cells in the upper part of the leaf more or less regularly rounded hexagonal, 8—10 μ. Seta reddish, capsule erect, symmetrical. Spores 15— —19 μ, very finely papillose, nearly smooth, mature in winter. — In low tufts or mats on damp, bare soil and rocks, etc. from the lowlands to the mountains.

Frequent. **S.** *Sk.—Dlr., Ång., TL., Öl.?, Gtl.* **N.** *ÖFld.—Fnm.* **F.** *Al., Ik., Ob., Ks.* **D.** in all provinces. (Europe, Asia, Macaronesia, North America).

Lindberg (in Bot. Not., 1887) has described var. **alpestris** with narrower leaves and border, thinner nerve. Is found in N. *STrd.*: Kongsvold in rock crevices. — Var. **gymnandrus** (Buse) Ruthe in Hedwigia, 1870; (*F. gymnandrus* Buse, Musc. Neerl. Exs.). — Fig. 1 C, c. — Antheridia naked in the axils of the leaves below the gynoecium. Leaves like those of the type. Grows on stones and wood by streams but is also found on damp limestone rocks. Scattered localities but more rare than the type.

5. F. viridulus (Web. et Mohr) Wg., Fl. Lapp., 1812; (*Dicranum viridulum* Web. et Mohr, Bot. Taschb., 1807; *F. impar* Mitt. in Journ. Linn. Soc. Bot., 1885; *F. bryoides* var. *Hedwigii* Limpr., Laubm., 1887; *F. bryoides* var. *viridulus* Broth., Laubm. Fennosk., 1923). — Fig. 1 E.

Dioicous or autoicous. Antheridium and archegonium usually terminal on separate plants. ♂ plants present either as small, bud-shaped dwarf male plants in the radicles of the ♀ plants or as larger individuals, — androecia rarely occur in the axils of the basal leaves. Leaves like those of *F. bryoides* but the border is narrower and usually slightly denticulate; in the upper leaves the border ends in or just below the apex, cells in upper part of leaf 10—12 μ. Capsule erect or somewhat inclined, seta yellow or reddish. Spores 12—16 μ. — Grows on similar substrata as the preceding species but on finer, more clayey earth.

Scattered localities. **S.** *Sk.—PL.* **N.** *ÖFld., Akh., VFld., Busk.* **F.** *Al.—Ks.* **D.** *Fy., Sj., Flst., Brnh.* (Europe, Macaronesia, North Africa, Asia, North America).

Nearly related to *F. bryoides*; the leaf cells are a little larger and the spores somewhat smaller. *F. bryoides* usually has numerous ♂ buds in the axils of the leaves.

6. F. haraldi (Lindb.) Limpr., Laubm., 1903; (*Schistophyllum Haraldi* Lindb. in Bot. Not., 1887) — Fig. 2 A.

Dioicous. Closely allied to *F. bryoides* and *F. viridulus* but usually smaller. The leaves at margin very finely and sparsely denticulate, the border of the upper leaves vanishing 6 or more cells below the apex; nerve thin, ending 3—1 cells below the apex; the cells are thin-walled, in upper part of the leaf 11—15 μ, slightly larger than those of *F. viridulus*. Seta reddish, capsule erect.— Plants pale green, decumbent or erect. Is found on calcareous soil together with other mosses, e. g. *Tortella* or *Weissia* sp., or in separate loose tufts.

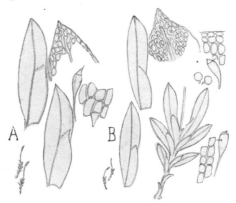

Fig. 2 A *Fissidens haraldi*, from spec. orig., B *F. pusillus*.

Very rare. **S.** *Öl.* (det. R. Potier de la Varde), **F.** *Nyl.* (Not found outside Scandinavia).

7. **F. incurvus** Starke in Web. et Mohr, Bot. Taschenb., 1807; (*F. bryoides* var. *incurvus* Hook. et Tayl., Musc. Brit., 1818; *F. viridulus* var. *incurvus* Wils., Br. Brit., 1855; *Schistophyllum incurvum* Lindb., Musci Scand., 1879; *F. viridulus* ssp. *incurvus* Waldh. in C. Jens. Skand. Bladmossfl., 1939).

Close to F. *viridulus* but differs in the smaller leaf cells, 8—10 μ, the horizontal or cernuous, usually strongly curved capsule. Occurs on clay banks, etc.

Recorded from **N**. *Akh*. However, I have not seen typical specimens from Fenno-scandia. (South, Central, and West Europe, Macaronesia, North Africa, Asia, North America).

8. F. pusillus Wils. ex. Milde, Br. Sil., 1869. — Fig. 2 B.

Dioicous, rarely autoicous. ♂ plants minute or larger. Leaves of ♀ plants in 2—4 pairs, the uppermost leaves longly lanceolate, obtuse or acute; margin entire or at apex finely crenulate; border narrow, vanishing far below the apex, on dorsal lamina the border ending about the middle or lacking in lower leaves; cells in upper part of the leaf 6—12 μ, more or less square, rectangular or indistinctly hexagonal, — the terminal cells are like the other cells of the leaf. Capsule erect or slightly inclined. Spores of different size, the largest about 16—20 μ, very finely papillose, nearly smooth, mature in July or August, seldom to November. — Very small, dark-green plants. solitary or gregarious on wet, siliceous stones or on rocks in streams.

Scattered localities in the southern part of the territory. **S**. *Sk.—Dlr*. **N**. *Akh*., *VFld.*, *Busk.*, *Tel*. **F**. *Al*. **D**. *Brnh*. (Europe, Algeria, Asia Minor, North America).

9. F. minutulus Sull. sec. Braithw., Mem. Am. Acad., 1848; (Braithw., Brit. Moss-Fl., 1887) — Fig. 1 F.

Dioicous or autoicous. Androecium terminal on basal branches of ♀ plants, on separate dwarf male plants or on larger plants. Is very nearly related to the preceding species but is usually more minute. The leaves are more erect, narrower and gradually tapering to a more acute point, the cells are somewhat larger, 7—14 μ, usually hexagonal but often irregular and of different size, — the terminal cells are elongate and different from the other cells of the leaf. The lid is obliquely rostrate, more than $\frac{1}{2}$ the length of the capsule. (*F. pusillus* has a shorter lid which is less than $\frac{1}{2}$ the length of the capsule). The spores are smaller, the largest are 13—15 μ. — Very small plants in loose, light-green carpets on wet, calcareous rocks.

Scattered localities in lime-rich districts of the south part of the territory. **S**. *Sk.—Dls.*, *Vg*. **N**. *Busk*. **D**. *Jl.*, *Fy.*, *Sj.*, *Brnh*. (Europe, North America).

According to R. Braithwaite and R. Potier de la Varde, *F. minutulus* has more pairs of leaves than *F. pusillus*. I have not observed this in Swedish specimens. ♀ plants have few pairs of leaves, sterile plants of both species may have several pairs of leaves.

Sect. III. A l o m a : Leaves regularly crenulate all round, not bordered. Sporophyte terminal. Peristome teeth spirally thickened and papillose above. — Minute plants on soil.

10. F. exilis Hedw., Sp. Musc., 1801; (*F. Bloxami* Wils. in Lond. Journ. Bot., 1845; *Schistophyllum exile* Lindb., Musci Scand., 1879). — Fig. 3 A.

Dioicous or autoicous. Androecium bud-like from the base of the ♀ plant or on dwarf male plants in the radicles of larger plants. Leaves in 2—4 pairs, the upper leaves linear-lanceolate, the margin finely and evenly serrulate or crenulate, dorsal lamina not reaching the base of the leaf; nerve percurrent or ending below the apex; cells in the upper part of the leaf 10—12 (—18) μ, irregularly hexagonal. Capsule erect and symmetrical. Spores 8—10 μ, yellowish, nearly smooth, mature in winter or in spring. — Our smallest species of this genus, 1—2 mm high, is usually found in sparse colonies on clayey ground, on bare soil, on edges of ditches, etc.

Scattered localities. **S.** *Sk.* — *Dsl., Nrk., Vstm., Öl., Gtl.* **N.** *ÖFld., Akh., Busk.* **F.** *Al., Ab., Nyl., Ka., St., Ta.* **D.** *Jl., Fy., Sj., Flst.* (Europe).

Sect. IV. Serridium: Leaves serrate or crenulate all round, not bordered of narrow, linear cells. Sporophyte lateral or terminal. Peristome teeth nodulose above. — ± tall plants on soil, rarely on rocks.

11. F. osmundoides Hedw., Sp. Musc., 1801; (*Schistophyllum osmundoides* Lindb., Musci Scand., 1879). — Fig. 3 B.

Dioicous, acrocarpous. Androecium and gynoecium terminal. Leaves lanceolate-lingulate, abruptly narrowed, shortly acuminate; margin evenly and finely serrulate or crenulate; nerve ending a little below the apex; cells in the upper part of the leaf irregular and varying in size between 10 and 20 μ, at margin somewhat smaller. Capsule on a terminal seta, erect or slightly inclined, usually symmetrical, calyptra mitriform. Spores 18—24 μ, finely papillose. — In close mats or tufts, stems several cm high, matted together with brown rhizoids. On damp humus, in rock crevices, on stones by streams, etc., from the lowlands to the alpine region.

Widespread but scattered. **S. N. F. D.** in all provinces. (Europe, Asia, North America, Greenland).

When sterile, this species can be confused with *F. cristatus*; both occur in rock crevices. However, *F. cristatus* has distinctly irregularly serrated leaves and a border of paler, more incrassate cells at margins; the areolation of *F. cristatus* is smaller than that of *F. osmundoides*. — *F. taxifolius* has finely and evenly serrate or crenulate leaves, but the leaves are narrower than those of *F. osmundoides* and the nerve is percurrent or excurrent.

12. F. taxifolius Hedw., Sp. Musc., 1801; (*Schistophyllum taxifolium* La Pyl. in Desv. Journ. Bot., 1813). — Fig. 3 E.

Dioicous or autoicous. Androecium bud-like in the radicles at the base of the stem, gynoecium axillary near the base. Leaves lanceolate-lingulate, margin finely and evenly serrulate or crenulate all round; nerve excurrent or percurrent; cells in the upper part of the leaf somewhat irregular, about 9—10 μ, thin-walled, at margins more incrassate and often slightly paler. Capsule variously inclined and sometimes slightly curved, seta inserted close to base of stem. Spores 14—20 μ, nearly smooth, mature in autumn. — In loose or compact tufts with procumbent or erect stems. Occurs on loam or calcareous soil in somewhat damp, shaded habitats, in the South on bare ground of beech woods.

Common in the South, rare towards the North. **S.** *Sk.* — *Vrm., Gstr., Öl., Gtl.* **N.** *ÖFld., Akh., Busk., NTrd.* **F.** *Al., Ab., Nyl.* **D.** in all provinces. (Europe, Asia, Macaronesia, North America).

For the differences between this species and *F. osmundoides, F. adianthoides,* and *F. cristatus* see the note under the respective species.

13. F. cristatus Wils. in Kew Journ. Bot., 1857; (*F. decipiens* DNot. in Piccone Elen. Musch., 1863; *F. rupestris* Wils., Musc. Brit. 1879; *Schistophyllum decipiens* Lindb., Musci Scand., 1879). — Fig. 3 D.

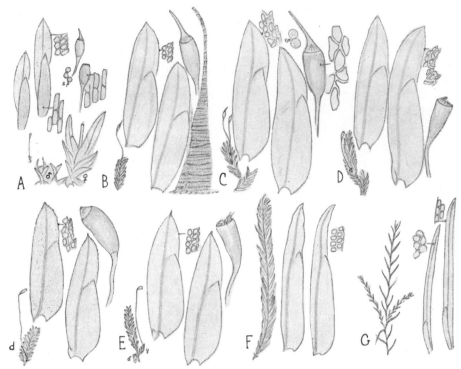

Fig. 3 A *Fissidens exilis*,   B *F. osmundoides*,   C *F. adianthoides*,   D *F. cristatus*,
d var. *mucronatus*,   E *F. taxifolius*,   F *F. polyphyllus*,   G *Octodiceras fontanum*.

Dioicous, rarely autoicous. Androecia and archegonia in axils of the leaves.
Leaves lanceolate-lingulate, shortly acuminate, margins towards apex irregularly serrate, below minutely serrulate or crenulate; nerve ending just
below the apex or excurrent; cells in upper part of the leaf irregular, 9—12 μ,
the marginal cells rounded, strongly incrassate, usually distinctly paler.
Capsule slightly inclined, seta red, inserted laterally. — Tufts dense, green
or brownish green, stems 1—several cm high, erect, rarely decumbent.
Occurs especially on calcareous substrata, dry soil or rock crevices, etc.

Frequent in suitable habitats. **S.** *Sk.* — *Upl., Dlr., Öl., Gtl.* **N.** *ÖFld., VAgd.,
Rog., Hord., Möre, Nrdl.* **F.** *Al., Ab., Nyl., Ka.* **D.** *Brnh.* (Europe, Azores, Asia
to China, Japan, India, Java, North America).

A variable species. It grows in large, compact, brownish green tufts in rock
crevices, etc.; on dry soil it is often more or less decumbent and the tufts are smaller
and lighter green. This plant is very like *F. taxifolius*, with which it is often growing.
However *F. taxifolius* has the leaf margin evenly crenulate or serrulate all round;
F. cristatus has the upper part of the leaf irregularly serrate and the leaf margin
bordered by a band of lighter colored, incrassate cells. Var. *mucronatus* (Breidl.)
Waldh. — Fig. 3 D, d. — Is a form with the nerve percurrent or excurrent. Such
forms are in the territory found especially on soil.

14. F. adianthoides Hedw., Sp. Musc., 1801. — Fig. 3 C.

Dioicous or autoicous, pleurocarpous. Androecia and archegonia in axils of the leaves. Leaves lanceolate-lingulate, acute, towards apex sharply and irregularly serrate, below minutely serrulate or crenulate; nerve percurrent or ending below the apex; cells of varying dimensions in the upper part of the leaf, c. 14—20 μ, marginal cells usually a little paler and ± more incrassate. Capsule erect or slightly inclined, seta inserted laterally. — Usually in loose tufts, several cm high, green, blackish-green at base, stem mostly more or less erect. Is found in bogs or marshes or on damp or wet soil, often near streams, from the lowlands to the mountains but not above the wood limit.

Common. **S. N. F. D.** in the whole territory. (Europe, Macaronesia, Algeria, North America).

Usually a large and distinct species with sharply serrulate leaves towards the apex and with slightly paler border at margins. Small sterile forms with less serrulate leaves can be confused with *F. taxifolius* and perhaps also with *F. osmundoides*. But in the tufts there are always some leaves with more distinctly serrulate margins and with more or less pale border. *F. adianthoides* has also a characteristic form of the leaves; see fig. 3 C. — From *F. cristatus* it is distinguished by larger, nearly uniform leaf cells.

15. F. polyphyllus Wils., Msc. in Br. Eur., 1851; (*F. asplenioides* var. β *polyphyllus* Wils., Br. Brit., 1855). — Fig. 3 F.

Dioicous. Androecia and gynoecia axillary from the upper part of the stem. Leaves long, narrowly lanceolate-lingulate, margins finely and evenly serrulate, at point usually with a few denticulations, the apical lamina as a rule shorter than the boat-formed part; nerve strong, ending below the apex; cells with the walls uniformly thickened, smooth or slightly mamillose, cells at margin 8—9 μ, toward the nerve becoming larger, 12—16 μ. Capsule on a yellowish seta, lateral. — A very robust species, the stem is often more than 15 cm long, prostrate or pendulous. Occurs on wet or submerged rocks.

Very rare. **N.** *Rog.* (West and South-West Europe, Macaronesia).

2. Octodiceras Brid., Sp. Musc., 1806.

Autoicous. Leaves with well developed lamellae, the apical part much lengthened, 2—3 times longer than the boat-formed part. Capsule small, symmetrical, elliptical, without stomata, seta short and thick. Stem without central strand. Aquatic mosses with slender, floating stems.

15. O. fontanum (La Pyl.) Lindb., Bidr. Moss. Syn., 1863; (*Skitophyllum fontanum* La Pyl. in Desv. Journ. Bot., 1813; *Fontinalis Juliana* Savi, Bot. Etrusc., 1818; *Fissidens Julianus* Schimp. in Fl., 1838; *Schistophyllum Julianum* Lindb., Musci Scand., 1879). — Fig. 3 G.

Androecium and gynoecium terminal on short axillary branches. Leaves distant, spreading, elongate-lanceolate, entire, apex subobtuse, the apical lamina 2—3 times longer than the boat-formed part; nerve ending below the apex; marginal cells small, about 8 μ, cells rapidly increasing in size towards the nerve. Capsule elliptical with a long lid; seta short and thick; peristome imperfect, teeth truncate, roughly papillose. — Floating plants on submerged rocks, roots, etc. in fresh as well as in brackish water.

Scattered. **S.** *Sk., Sm., Vg., Nrk., Srm., Upl., Nb.* **F.** *Ta., Ik.* (Europe, North Africa, North America, Mexico, Chile).

Order 2. **Dicranales**

The terminal cell of the stem trilateral. Leaves usually smooth, lanceolate to subulate. Peristome single, teeth 16. Acrocarpous.

Fam. II. **Archidiaceae**

Cleistocarpous, perennial, terrestrial mosses. Stem leaves rather small, apical and perichaetial leaves larger, lanceolate-acuminate with a more or less sheathing base, basal cells parenchymatous, towards the apex prosenchymatous. Capsule globose, the wall single-layered, seta thick, short, inserted in the rounded vaginula, calyptra very thin, enclosing the capsule, finally tearing irregularly, the remains adherent to the base of the capsule. Spores very large, between 100 and 200 µ.

Fig. 4
Archidium alternifolium.

3. Archidium Brid. Br. Univ. 1826.

With characteristics of the family.

1. A. alternifolium (Hedw.) Schimp., Syn. Musc., 1860; (*Phascum alternifolium* Hedw., Sp. Musc., 1801; *A. phascoides* Brid. in Br. Univ. 1826). — Fig. 4.

Stem leaves lanceolate from oval base, margin denticulate especially at apex; cells smooth, fairly thick-walled, those at apex and beside the nerve prosenchymatous; nerve percurrent or ending just below the apex. Apical leaves lanceolate — subulate, with the nerve excurrent. Capsule relatively small, globose with transparent walls. Spores usually 16—20 in each capsule, yellowish, smooth. — Low tufts or mats, stems about 1 cm long, growing on damp, often sandy ground, beside lakes, on damp moorland soil, etc.

Scattered. **S.** *Sk.—Gstr., Gtl.* **N.** *ÖFld., VFld.* **F.** *Al., Ab.* **D.** *Jl., Fy.* (Europe, Azores, North America).

Fam. III. **Ditrichaceae**

Autoicous or dioicous. Apical leaves usually larger than the lower leaves. Stem leaves from broad base usually long, subulate, with serrulate apex, seldom shortly ovate-lanceolate; nerve in cross section of heterogeneous cells, usually with guide cells and two stereid bands, often strong, excurrent or ending in or below the apex; cells in the upper part of the leaves quadrate — shortly rectangular, sometimes rounded and very irregular; at the base cells more elongate, sometimes enlarged and more or less hyaline, alar cells not differentiated. Capsule cleistocarpous or stegocarpous, erect and symmetrical or slightly inclined and asymmetrical; lid conical with or without a longer or shorter beak; calyptra cucullate, or in *Sporledera*, mitriform; annulus usually of large cells, separating. Peristome with a taller or shorter basal membrane, teeth papillose, more seldom striated, deeply divided or perforated.

I Capsule cleistocarpous, immersed in the perichaetial
  leaves; seta very short
    1 Stomata only at base of capsule; calyptra cucullate .... 4. *Pleuridium*
    2 Stomata in the middle of the capsule; calyptra
      mitriform .... 5. *Sporledera*
II Capsule stegocarpous; seta long
    1 The neck of the capsule half or more of the whole
      length of the capsule .... 6. *Trematodon*
    2 The neck of the capsule short
      a Leaves in several ranks
        b Capsule strumose, sulcate, mostly inclined and
          somewhat curved; cells in upper part of leaf re-
          gularly quadrate .... 7. *Ceratodon*
        bb Capsule not strumose, erect or slightly inclined,
          smooth or wrinkled when dry; cells in upper
          part of leaf quadrate to rectangular, more or
          less irregular
        c Plants glaucous with cobweb-thin threads .... 8. *Saelania*
        cc Plants green, not glaucous .... 9. *Ditrichum*
      aa Leaves distinctly 2-ranked (distichous) .... 10. *Distichium*

4. **Pleuridium** Brid., Mont. Musc., 1819.

Cleistocarpous earth mosses. Perichaetial leaves from oval sheathing base narrowed in a long, subulate, more or less serrulate point formed by the excurrent nerve. Capsule ovoid with a short, abrupt point, stomata only at the base of the capsule. Calyptra cucullate.

I Autoicous. The sheathing base of the perichaetial lea-
  ves short, rapidly narrowed to a long subula .... 1. *P. subulatum*
II Paroicous. The sheathing base of the perichaetial lea-
  ves as long as, or only a little shorter than the subula ...... 2. *P. acuminatum*

1. **P. subulatum** (Hedw.) Lindb. in Öfv. K. V. A. Förh., 1863; (*Phascum subulatum* Hedw., Sp. Musc. 1801; *Phascum alternifolium* Kaulf. in Sturm, Deutsch. Fl. 1815; *P. alternifolium* Brid., Musc. Resc., Suppl. 1819). — Fig. 5 A.

Stem leaves small, lanceolate—subulate, cells in the whole leaf quadrate or shortly rectangular. The sheathing part of the perichaetial leaves hardly reaches the base of the capsule. Towards the base of the leaves the marginal cells are narrow, becoming enlarged and partly bistratose towards the nerve; nerve wide, indistinct. Androecia bud-shaped in the axils of the stem leaves below the gynoecium. Capsule ovoid, lid with a short beak. Spores 24—28 μ, yellow, papillose, mature in summer. — Soft, green mats or scattered on ± damp soil.

Scattered in the lowlands. **S.** *Sk.—Hls., Öl., Gtl.* **N.** *ÖFld.—STrd.* **F.** *Al., Ab., St., Ta., Kl.* **D.** the whole country. (Europe, Asia, North Africa, Macaronesia, North America).

2. **P. acuminatum** Lindb., Öfv. K. V. A. Förh., 1863; (*Phascum subulatum* Bruch in Flora, 1825; *Astomum subulatum* Hampe in Flora, 1837; *P. subulatum* Rabenh., Deutschl. Krypt. Fl., 1879). — Fig. 5 B.

Stem leaves small, lanceolate — subulate; cells in the whole leaf quadrate

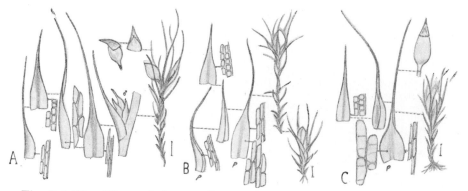

Fig. 5 A *Pleuridium subulatum*,   B *P. acuminatum*,   C *Sporledera palustris*.

or shortly rectangular. The sheathing part of the perichaetial leaves nearly reaching the end of the capsule; nerve, cells, capsule and spores like those of the preceding species. The antheridia naked in the axils of the apical leaves below the gynoecium. — In dense, soft, green mats or scattered on slightly moist soil.

Widespread but more rare than the foregoing species. **S.** *Sk.—Dls., Srm., Öl., Gtl.* **N.** *ÖFld., Tel., Hord., SoFj.* **F.** *Al., Ab.* **D.** *Jl., Brnh.* (Europe, Macaronesia, Algeria, East China, North America).

5.   **Sporledera** Hampe in Linnaea, 1837.

Cleistocarpous, paroicous earth mosses. Perichaetial leaves from ovate sheathing base rapidly narrowed to a long subulate point consisting mainly of the excurrent nerve. Capsule ovoid, beaked, stomata in or above the middle of the capsule. Calyptra mitriform, many-lobed, seldom entire.

1.   **S. palustris** (Br. et Sch.) Hampe in litt. C. Müll., Syn. Musc., 1848; (*Phascum palustre* Br. et Sch. in Mem. Soc. Mus. Strasb., 1827; *Astomum palustre* Hampe in Flora, 1837; *Bruchia palustris* C. Müll., Syn. Musc., 1848; *Pleuridium palustre* Br. Eur., 1850). — Fig. 5 C.

Stem leaves small, lanceolate—subulate; cells in the whole leaf quadrate or shortly rectangular, incrassate. Perichaetial leaves from wide, sheathing base rapidly narrowed to a long subulate, serrulate awn; marginal cells narrow, much enlarged towards the base and nerve. Capsule ovoid with a short point. Calyptra small, mitriform, usually many-lobed, covering the top of the capsule. Spores 24—30 µ, yellow, papillose, mature in early summer. — In soft, green mats on damp humus.

Rare. **S.** *Sk., Vg.* **N.** *VFld.* (Europe, North America).

6.   **Trematodon** Michx., Fl. Bor. Amer., 1803.

Autoicous, more rarely dioicous; ♂ shoots bud-shaped, at the base of the ♀ shoots or sometimes in *T. ambiguus* ♂ and ♀ shoots separate but in the same tuft. Leaves smooth, entire; nerve excurrent. Capsule slightly curved and club-shaped, neck long, slender, half or more of the whole length of the cap-

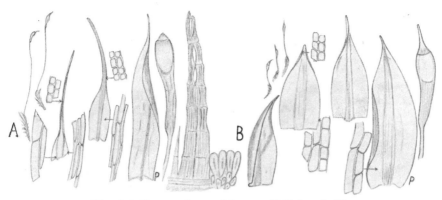

Fig. 6 A *Trematodon ambiguus*, B *T. brevicollis*.

sule; annulus absent, numerous stomata in the neck of the capsule. Peristome purple, with basal membrane, teeth entire, more or less perforated along the middle or divided nearly to the base, with coarse vertical striations. Lid rostrate. Calyptra cucullate. Spores large, coarsely papillose.

I Neck more than half of the whole capsule, leaves with
   sheathing base rapidly narrowed to a long subula .... 1. *T. ambiguus*
II Neck about half the length of the capsule, leaves
   ovate, rapidly narrowed to a short point .... 2. *T. brevicollis*

1. T. ambiguus (Hedw.) Hornsch. in Flora, 1819; (*Dicranum ambiguum* Hedw., Sp. Musc., 1801; *T. elongatus* Hag. in K. N. V. Selsk. Skr. 1915). —Fig. 6 A.

Leaves from an appressed sheathing base narrowed above to a long spreading subula, apex often faintly denticulate; nerve strong, constituting most of the apex; cells in lower part of the leaf elongate, thin-walled, — in upper part quadrate or shortly rectangular. Seta 2—3 cm long, yellow, capsule slightly curved, the neck strumose, a little longer than the capsule itself. Peristome teeth divided almost to the basal membrane or irregularly perforated. Spores about 30 μ, yellowish green, with large papillae. — In low mats on moist clayey humus.

Rare, scattered from lowlands to mountains, seldom above the tree limit. **S.** *Sk.—Nb.* **N.** *ÖFld.—Nrdl.* **F.** in most of the provinces. **D.** *Jl.* (North and Central Europe, Japan, North America).

2. T. brevicollis Hornsch. in Flora, 1819. — Fig. 6 B.

Leaves appressed, widely ovate-lanceolate, concave, abruptly narrowed to a short, usually obtuse point; nerve strong, indistinctly delimited, ending in the apex, cells in the whole leaf quadrate to shortly rectangular, smaller towards the apex. Seta yellow, short, a few mm long; capsule brownish, arcuate; neck as long as the capsule, without struma. Peristome like that of the preceding species, with perforated teeth. Spores 54—60 μ, coarsely papillose. — A low-growing species on earth or gravel.

Rare, on mountains above the tree limit. **S.** *TL.* **N.** *Opl., STrd., Nrdl., Trs.* **F.** *Le.* (North and Central Europe, Central Asia, Greenland).

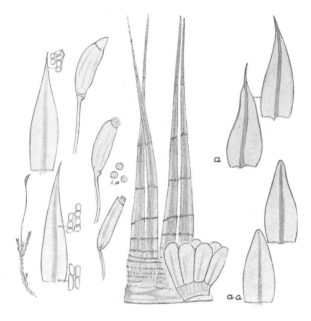

Fig. 7 *Ceratodon purpureus*, a var. *conicus*, aa var. *obtusifolius*.

7.   **Ceratodon** Brid., Br. Univ., 1826.

Dioicous. Leaves lanceolate, with revolute margins; cells in the whole leaf homogeneous, regularly quadrate above, shortly rectangular below, incrassate; nerve strongly excurrent or ending just below the apex. Perichaetial leaves longer than the stem leaves, sheathing. Capsule on a purple or yellowish red seta, inclined, when dry sulcate and furrowed, usually with a distinct struma. Annulus of large cells. Peristome with basal membrane, teeth papillose, deeply divided, when dry the points are curved inwards. Lid conical.

1.   **C. purpureus** (Hedw.) Brid., Br. Univ., 1826; (*Dicranum purpureum* Hedw., Sp. Musc., 1801). — Fig. 7.

♂ and ♀ plants usually in separate tufts, androecia and gynoecia at stem apex. Leaves lanceolate with the margins recurved to just below the apex, which bears a few obtuse denticulations. Nerve strong, ending in the point or excurrent. Capsule brownish red or yellowish brown; peristome teeth red-brown, with a paler border from the base to above the middle. In loose glossy mats of a dull green, brownish or reddish green colour, on all kinds of substratum, especially open, sandy or burnt soil.

Common from the lowlands to high up in the mountains. **S., N., F., D.** in all provinces. (Cosmopolitan).

A polymorphous species with many described forms and varieties of more or less value. — Var. **conicus** (Hampe) Hag.; (*Trichostomum conicum* Hampe, *C. conicus* Lindb.). — Fig. 7 a. — Leaves broadly lanceolate; nerve strong, longly excurrent. Capsule small, more or less erect; peristome teeth with or without a very narrow and slightly paler border. — In low, dark green mats about 1 cm high, on dry soil. — Var. **dimorphus** (Philib.) C. Jens. Leaves small, concave, margins nearly flat. Peristome teeth without paler border. — In low mats about

1 cm high, in subalpine reg. — Var. **obtusifolius** Limpr. — Fig. 7 aa. — Nerve usually ending below the obtuse point. — In sterile mats several cm high. — Var. **xanthopus** Sull. Leaves narrow, lanceolate. Peristome teeth with pale border only at the base.

8. Saelania Lindb., Utkast, 1878.

Autoicous. Antheridia at the apex of short branches below the gynoecium. Apical leaves from lanceolate base gradually narrowed in a long, erecto-patent, denticulate subula, margins flat or slightly recurved, occasionally bistratose; cells smooth, in the upper part of the leaf shortly rectangular or quadrate, towards the base more elongated, somewhat enlarged. Perichaetial leaves like the apical leaves. The lower leaves small, areolation homogeneous throughout, being shortly rectangular or quadrate. Capsule erect, symmetrical, oblong or cylindrical, slightly wrinkled when dry; peristome teeth papillose, usually divided to the base; lid shortly rostrate.

Fig. 8 *Saelania glaucescens.*

1. **S. glaucescens** (Hedw.) Broth. in Engl. et Prantl., Nat. Pfl. Fam., 1924; (*Trichostomum glaucescens* Hedw., Sp. Musc., 1801; *Ditrichum glaucescens* Hampe in Flora, 1867; S. *caesia* Lindb., Musci Scand., 1879). — Fig. 8.

Lower stem leaves very small, erecto-patent, at the apex longer, lanceolate, and somewhat crowded. Capsule yellowish green, oblong or cylindrical; peristome reddish-brown, teeth closely and highly papillose; lid somewhat darker than the capsule. Spores about 15 μ, faintly papillose, mature in summer. — In soft, bluish green tufts on ± dry, preferably calcareous soil, in rock crevices on road-sides, on edge of ditches, etc.

Common in subalpine region, rare in lowlands. **S.** *Boh., Vg.—TL.* **N.** *ÖFld.—Fnm.* **F.** in most provinces. (Europe, South Africa, Asia, North America, Greenland, Hawaii, New Zealand).

This species is easily recognized by the bluish green or bluish grey colour caused by fine fungal or algal threads which are usually copiously entwined round the stem and leaf bases. Cf. the hepatic genus *Anthelia*.

9. Ditrichum Timm. 1788; Hampe in Flora, 1867; (*Leptotrichum* Hampe in Linnaea, 1847).

Scandinavian species dioicous, except *D. pallidum*. Leaves from a ± broad base gradually narrowed to a usually long, fine, channelled, entire or serrate apex; nerve often broad and filling the apex, percurrent or excurrent; cells in the upper part of the leaf quadrate or shortly rectangular, in the lower part mostly rectangular, angular cells not distinct, except *D. flexicaule*. Capsule on a long, erect or slightly curved seta, symmetrical or somewhat asymmetrical. Peristome teeth papillose, divided nearly to the base; annulus of large cells.

I Upper leaves squarrose, when dry crisped, from a
   sheathing base abruptly narrowed to a long, fine
   subula .... 1. *D. cylindricum*
II Leaves from a broad, not sheathing base, gradually
   narrowed to a ± straight or slightly curved apex
   1 Tall tufts matted with tomentum; cells in the nar-
     rowed part of the leaf irregular, rectangular, triang-
     ular or quadrate .... 2. *D. flexicaule*
   2 Short tufts, not tomentose; leaf cells mostly regu-
     lar, rectangular
     a Autoicous; seta yellow; spores papillose .... 3. *D. pallidum*
     aa Dioicous; seta red at least at the base; spores
        smooth
        b Peristome reddish brown, highly and closely
          papillose
          c Leaves with flat margins .... 4. *D. heteromallum*
          cc Leaves with recurved margins .... 5. *D. pusillum*
        bb Peristome yellow, lowly and sparsely papillose,
           nearly smooth; leaves with recurved margins .... 6. *D. lineare*

1. **D. cylindricum** (Hedw.) Grout, Moss Fl., 1936; (*Trichostomum cylindri-
    cum* Hedw., Sp. Musc., 1801; *D. tenuifolium* Lindb., Musci Scand.,
    1879). — Fig. 9 A.
    The lower leaves small and erect, towards the apex becoming rapidly
larger, squarrose with a long, finely denticulate subula; cells in the upper
part of the leaf rectangular, basal cells beside the nerve elongate, becoming
shorter towards the margin. Capsule narrowly cylindrical, erect or slightly
curved, seta reddish at least at base. Peristome teeth closely papillose, reddish
brown, usually divided to the base, basal membrane short. Spores smooth,
11—14 μ, mature in early summer. — In low, yellowish green tufts on sandy
or loamy soil.

Scattered in the South, more common in the North. **S. N. F.** in most provinces.
D. *Jl.*, *Sj.* (Europe, Asia, North America).
    Var. **oblongum** (Lindb.) C. Jens.; (*Trichodon oblongus* Lindb., *D. tenuifolium*
var. *oblongum* Hag.). — Fig. 9 A, a. — A tall form ocurring in North Scandinavia and Spitsbergen. Capsule larger than the type. Spores to 16 or 19 μ.

2. **D. flexicaule** (Schleich.) Hampe in Flora, 1867; (*Didymodon flexicaulis*
    Schleich., Pl. Crypt. Helv., 1807; *Trichostomum flexicaule* Br. Eur.,
    1843). — Fig. 9 B.
    Leaves from a ± broad, lanceolate base, gradually narrowed to a long,
fine subula, crisped when dry; nerve broad, indistinct, excurrent; cells in
the upper part of the leaf small, irregular; basal cells beside the nerve elongate, becoming shorter towards the margin where there is often a narrow
border of linear cells. Seta red; capsule ovoid to cylindrical; peristome highly
and closely papillose, in the upper part colourless, towards the base reddish
brown, basal membrane short. Spores 8—12 μ, yellow, smooth, mature in
early summer. — In soft, yellowish or brownish green tufts, closely matted
with brown tomentum, on calcareous soil, rock crevices, etc.

Common in suitable habitats from the lowlands to high in the mountains. **S.
N. F.** in most provinces, **D.** *Jl.*, *Mö.*, *Brnh.* (Europe, Asia, Algeria, Canaries,
Madeira, North America, New Zealand).

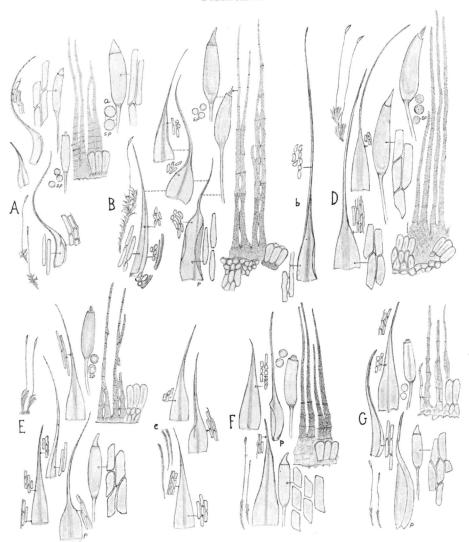

Fig. 9 A *Ditrichum cylindricum*, a var. *oblongum*, B *D. flexicaule*, b var. *sterilis*, D *D. pallidum*, E *D. heteromallum*, e var. *zonatum*, F *D. pusillum*, G *D. lineare*.

Var. **densum** (Br. Eur.) Braithw. Leaves short, erect, rigid. Tufts compact, tomentum extending high up the stems. In dry localities, often together with the type. — Var. **sterilis** DNot., Syll. Musc., 1838; (var. *longifolium* Zett., Musci and Hep. Oeland, 1869; *D. giganteum* Williams in Bull. N. Y. Gard.), — Fig. 9 B, b. — Leaves almost straight, with a very long subula, at apex distinctly denticulate, when dry the leaves are not crisped. Tufts lax, tall, yellowish brown, tomentose only near the base. A beautiful form of damper habitats.

3. D. pallidum (Hedw.) Hampe in Flora, 1867; (*Trichostomum pallidum*

Hedw., Sp. Musc., 1801; *Leptotrichum pallidum* Hampe in Linnaea, 1847). — Fig. 9 D.

Autoicous. Androecium bud-like in the axils of the apical leaves. Leaves often ± secund, from lanceolate base gradually narrowed to a long, slightly toothed, channelled apex; nerve broad, indistinct, excurrent; cells in the upper part of the leaves shortly rectangular or quadrate, basal cells beside the nerve enlarged, rectangular, becoming narrower at the margins. Capsule on a yellow seta, oblong-ovoid, slightly irregular, somewhat furrowed when dry and empty; peristome reddish brown, highly and closely papillose, teeth with a short basal membrane, divided into two filiform segments. Spores brown, closely papillose, 14—18 μ, mature in early summer. — In light-green, yellowish, glossy tufts on loam or calcareous soil, especially on bare soil in deciduous woods.

Rare. **S.** *Srm., Vb.* **D.** *Flst., Sj.* (Europe, Azores, Central Africa, North America).

4. D. heteromallum (Hedw.) E. G. Britton, N. Am. Fl., 1913; (*Weisia heteromalla* Hedw., Sp. Musc., 1801; *Didymodon homomallum* Hedw., Sp. Musc., 1801; *Trichostomum homomallum* Br. Eur., 1843; *D. homomallum* Hampe in Flora, 1867). — Fig. 9 E.

Leaves mostly secund, from lanceolate base gradually narrowed into a long, filiform, concave subula, margins plane, entire, apex slightly denticulate; nerve broad, indistinct, excurrent; cells in the upper part of the leaf shortly rectangular, towards the base elongate. Capsule narrowly oblong-ovoid; peristome yellowish red to brownish red, closely papillose, basal membrane short. Spores about 15 μ, mature in autumn. — In low, yellowish green, glossy tufts on damp, sandy soil.

Scattered to frequent from the lowlands to high up in the mountains. **S. N. F. D.** over the whole territory. (Europe, North America).

Var. **zonatum** (Brid.) Lindb., Musci Scand., 1879; (*W. zonata* Brid., Br. Univ., 1826; *D. zonatum* Limpr., Laubm. I., 1887; *D. vaginans* var. *zonatum* Hag. in K. N. V. Selsk. Skr., 1910). — Fig. 9 E, e. — Tufts up to more than 5 cm high, compact, yellowish green, somewhat glossy. Leaves short, straight or very slightly falcate, margin plane, apex channelled; nerve indistinct. Stem erect, fragile. Occurs only on rocks and in rock crevices in alpine regions. Rare. **S.** *LL.* **N.** *Busk., ÖAgd., Opl., Hord., Möre, Hdm., STrd.* **F.** *Ks., Lk., Le., Li.* (North, West and Central Europe, Pyrenees).

This form has a characteristic stratification inside the tufts, consisting of alternate light and dark striations. — Is perhaps a separate species, but so long as it is found only sterile, its position is difficult to determine.

5. D. pusillum (Hedw.) E. G. Britton, N. Am. Fl., 1913; (*Didymodon pusillus* Hedw., Sp. Musc., 1801; *Leptotrichum tortile* C. Müll., Syn. Musc., 1849; *D. tortile* Brockm., Laubm. Meckl., 1869). — Fig. 9 F.

Leaves from lanceolate base gradually narrowed to a channelled, less serrulate apex, margin narrowly recurved to below the middle; nerve distinct, ending in the apex or slightly excurrent; cells in the upper part of the leaf shortly rectangular or quadrate, towards the base of the leaf elongate. Capsule erect, cylindrical to shortly ovate; peristome brownish red, with a well developed basal membrane, teeth deeply divided, closely papillose. Spores nearly smooth, yellow, 11—15 μ, mature in autumn. — In low, dull green tufts on damp sandy ground.

Scattered. **S. N. F.** in most provinces, **D.** *Jl., Fy., Flst., Sj.* (Europe, Asia, Algeria, North America).

6.   D. lineare (Sw.) Lindb. in Acta Soc. Sc. Fenn., 1871; (*Didymodon lineare* Sw., Adnot. Bot., 1829; *Trichostomum vaginans* Sull., Musci Allegh., 1845; *D. vaginans* Hampe in Flora, 1867). — Fig. 9 G.

Leaves from lanceolate, somewhat concave base, gradually narrowed to a channelled, slightly serrulate subula, margin less revolute towards the middle; nerve distinct, ending in the point; cells like those of the preceding species. Capsule yellowish brown, erect, cylindrical; peristome smooth or slightly papillose, basal membrane short. Spores about 11 μ, yellowish, nearly smooth, mature in autumn. — In somewhat dense, slightly glossy, yellowish green tufts on sandy or loamy ground.

Rare, in subalpine region. **S.** *Vg.—TL.* **N.** ¦*ÖFld.—NTrd.* **F.** *Ks., Lk., Le., Li.* (North and Central Europe, North America).

10.   **Distichium** Br. Eur., 1846.

Autoicous, paroicous or synoicous. Leaves distichous, with broad, sheathing base, narrowed to a very long, rough subula; cells in the upper part of the leaf shortly rectangular or quadrate, — in the narrowed part cells irregularly triangular, quadrate or rectangular, — in the lower part, cells elongate, linear; nerve broad. Capsule erect or inclined on a slender seta; peristome irregularly divided or perforated, teeth striated or nearly smooth; annulus soon becoming loose; lid conical. Calyptra cucullate. In transverse section the stem is oval.

I   Leaves squarrose or reflexed; capsule erect and symmetri-
    cal or nearly so; spores   17—20   μ.................... 1. *D. capillaceum*
II Leaves more erect, not reflexed; capsule inclined, asymme-
    trical, ovate; spores more than 25 μ
    1 Peristome with 16 irregularly divided or perforated teeth.... 2. *D. inclinatum*
    2 Peristome 8-lobed.. 3. *D. hageni*

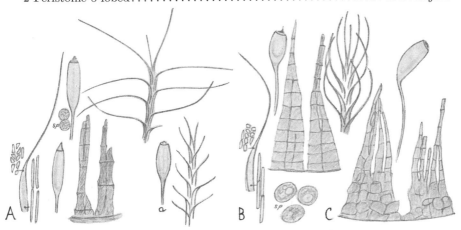

Fig. 10 A *Distichium capillaceum*, a var. *compactum*, B *D. inclinatum*, C *D. hageni*.

1. **D. capillaceum** (Hedw.) Br. Eur., 1846; (*Cynodontium capillaceum* Hedw., Sp. Musc., 1801; *Swartzia montana* Lindb., Musci Scand., 1879). — Fig. 10 A.

Autoicous or paroicous. Leaves from oval, whitish, sheathing base, rapidly narrowed to a long, fine, channelled rough subula; nerve broad, shortly excurrent. Capsule erect or very slightly curved, oblong- or ovate-cylindrical; peristome reddish, teeth irregularly split, narrowly and shortly striated. Spores 17—20 μ, papillose, mature in summer. — Tufts soft, glossy green, compact, 5—15 cm high, stems matted together with brown tomentum. Grows on calcareous soil, in rock crevices, etc.

Frequent in suitable habitats from the lowlands to high up in the mountains. **S. N. F. D.** throughout the whole territory (Cosmopolitan).

In arctic-alpine regions there are forms with shorter leaves in more compact tufts; the capsule also is often shorter. The extreme form is described as var. **compactum** (Hüb.) Dix.; (var. *brevifolium* Br. Eur.), but there is every gradation between it and the type. — Fig. 10 A, a.

2. **D. inclinatum** (Hedw.) Br. Eur., 1846; (*Cynodontium inclinatum* Hedw., Sp. Musc., 1801). — Fig. 10 B.

Leaves from lanceolate, only slightly whitish base, less abruptly narrowed to a long, fine, rough subula, the upper part of the leaf more erect than that of the preceding species. Capsule more or less inclined and asymmetrical; peristome brownish red, teeth broad, irregularly split or perforated. Spores large, 30—40 μ, mature in summer. — Tufts 2—4 cm high, tomentose only at the base. On damp calcareous soil.

Common in mountains, scattered localities in the lowlands. **S. N. F.** in most provinces. **D.** *Jl.*, *Sj.*, *Brnh.* (Europe, Morocco, North and Central Asia, Japan, North America).

3. **D. hageni** Ryan in Rev. Br., 1896. — Fig. 10 C.

Close to *D. inclinatum.* Capsule short- to oblong-oval; peristome red, in 8 groups, every group containing 2 irregularly split peristome teeth, the lower part of which is held together by the complete inner membrane. — Tufts low, seldom attaining a height of 5 cm.

Very rare. **S.** *Gstr.* **N.** *Fnm.* (North Europe, North Asia, Greenland, North America).

Fam. IV Seligeriaceae

Autoicous. Lower leaves mostly very small, becoming rapidly larger towards the stem apex. The upper leaves from a somewhat broader base, lanceolate or subulate, margin entire or serrulate; nerve ending in or below the apex, at the top often flattened and occupying the greater part of the awn, — in cross section the nerve consists of uniform cells; leaf cells smooth, in the upper part of the leaf mostly shortly rectangular or quadrate, towards the base the cells are enlarged and more elongate, angular cells distinct in *Blindia* and *Stylostegium* only. Capsule mostly smooth, with stomata; annulus absent; peristome when present reddish, teeth 16, longer or shorter, smooth, usually entire or rarely cleft, sometimes with nodes, when dry erect or recurved. Calyptra cucullate. (The genus *Brachydontium* differs from other genera in having striate capsules, campanulate calyptra and an annulus of large cells). Stems with central strand. Small plants (except *Blindia*), growing on damp limestone or sandstone rocks.

I   Leaves with well differentiated angular cells
   1 Dioicous; seta long, peristome present....................... 11. *Blindia*
   2 Autoicous; capsule on a short seta, often enclosed in the
     large perichaetial leaves, peristome lacking............... 12. *Stylostegium*
II Leaves without or with slightly developed angular cells;
   mostly very small plants
   1 Calyptra cucullate, capsule smooth or, when dry, in-
     distinctly furrowed .... 13. *Seligeria*
   2 Calyptra campanulate, capsule striate, when dry deeply
     furrowed... 14. *Brachydontium*

11. Blindia Br. Eur., 1846.

Dioicous. Leaves with distinct, coloured, angular cells. Seta long; capsule pyriform; peristome teeth lanceolate, smooth.

1. B. acuta (Hedw.) Br. Eur., 1846; (*Weisia acuta* Hedw., Sp. Musc., 1801; *Seligeria acuta* DNot., Epil., 1869). — Fig. 11 B.
Leaves from lanceolate, concave base, rapidly narrowed into a long, subulate or obtuse apex, entire or with few teeth; nerve at the top flattened and filling up the greater part of the awn; cells narrow-rectangular, thick-walled, at the base rows of shorter, orange or brownish cells, — angular cells enlarged, forming a well differentiated, coloured group. Capsule pyriform, neck short, with stomata; seta long, straight or curved; peristome reddish brown, teeth lanceolate, usually perforated. Spores about 12 μ, nearly smooth, mature in summer. — Tufts 1—10 cm high, glossy, light or brownish green, darker below; on damp or wet rocks, etc.

Widespread in the subalpine region. **S. N. F.** in most provinces. **D.** *Brnh.* (Europe, Azores, Madeira, Asia, North America, Greenland).

12. Stylostegium Br. Eur., 1846.

Autoicous. Perichaetial leaves very large; angular cells distinct, hyaline or coloured. Peristome teeth absent.

1. S. caespiticium (Schwaegr.) Br. Eur., 1846; (*Anoectangium caespiticium* Schwaegr. in Web. et Mohr, Bot. Taschenb., 1807; *Blindia caespiticia* C. Müll., Deutschl. Moose, 1853). — Fig. 11 C.
Perichaetial leaves enclosing the whole or nearly the whole capsule; the other leaves similar to those of *Blindia acuta*. Capsule on a very short seta, subsphaerical, after the fall of the lid wide-mouthed; lid united with the columella, which lengthens after the maturity of the spores, finally both falling off together; peristome lacking. Spores about 14 μ, finely papillose, mature in summer. — Tufts ¼—4 cm high, glossy, brownish green. On shady limestone or schistose rocks in the upper part of the forest region.

Rare, but not uncommon in suitable habitats in the mountains. **S.** *Hjd.—TL.* **N.** *Hord.—Trs.* (North, West and Central Europe).

13. Seligeria Br. Eur., 1846.

Autoicous. Leaves without or with very slightly differentiated angular cells. Very small mosses on moist or wet, seldom dripping, more or less shady, calciferous rocks.

I Columella lengthened; spores 18—30 μ
  1 Capsule wide-mouthed, campanulate after the fall of the lid; peristome teeth broadly obtuse
    a The apex of the leaves with a very long, bristle- or thread-like prolongation ....1. *S. carniolica*
    aa Leaves without a thread-like prolongation
      b Spores 20—27 μ ....2. *S. oelandica*
      bb Spores 27—31 μ; mountain plant ....3. *S. lapponica*
  2 Capsule hemispherical after the fall of the lid; peristome teeth lanceolate; spores 18—21 μ....................4. *S. tristichoides*
II Columella short; spores 8—18 μ
  1 Seta erect or nearly so, not recurved when moist
    a Nerve flattened at the apex and filling up the awn
      b Leaves entire, alar cells slightly differentiated, quadrate
        c Seta 2—3 mm long, somewhat curved; capsule reaching over the perichaetial leaves....................5. *S. polaris*
        cc Seta straight, 1—1½ mm long; capsule partially immersed ....6. *S. subimmersa*
      bb Leaves serrulate, alar cells not differentiated
        c Peristome absent; spores 8—10 μ ....7. *S. doniana*
        cc Peristome present; spores 14—18 μ ....8. *S. calcarea*
    aa Nerve not flattened at the top, percurrent or ending below the point
      b Capsule obovoid — pyriform; peristome teeth about 0,10 mm; seta straight ....9. *S. pusilla*
      bb Capsule obovoid; peristome teeth about 0,18 mm; seta thin, somewhat curved
        c Leaves narrow, linear, serrulate ....10. *S. brevifolia*
        cc Leaves lanceolate, entire ....11. *S. diversifolia*
  2 Seta recurved when moist
    a Leaves shortly subulate; nerve percurrent or ending below the point ....12. *S. campylopoda*
    aa Leaves entire, with a long subula consisting mainly of the nerve ....13. *S. recurvata*

1. S. carniolica (Breidl. et Beck) n. comb. (*Trochobryum carniolicum* Breidl. et Beck in Verh. d. Zool.—Bot. Ges. in Wien, 1884). — Fig. 11 D.

Lower leaves small, broadly lanceolate; upper leaves abruptly larger, from sheathing base with very long, bristle- or thread-like subula composed of the excurrent nerve. Seta thick; capsule globular, campanulate when empty and dry; lid united with the columella which lengthens after the ripening of the spores, finally both falling away together; peristome red or orange, teeth broad, obtuse. Spores 20—27 μ, finely papillose, mature in summer. Brownish green tufts, a few mm high, on limestone rocks.

Very rare. Only one locality known in North Europe. **S.** *Gtl.* (A few known localities in West and Central Europe.)

2. S. oelandica Jens. et Med. in Bot. Not., 1929. — Tab. 11 E.

Leaves from ovate-lanceolate base gradually narrowed to a stout awn; nerve broad, filling up the greater part of the awn; basal cells elongate, rect-

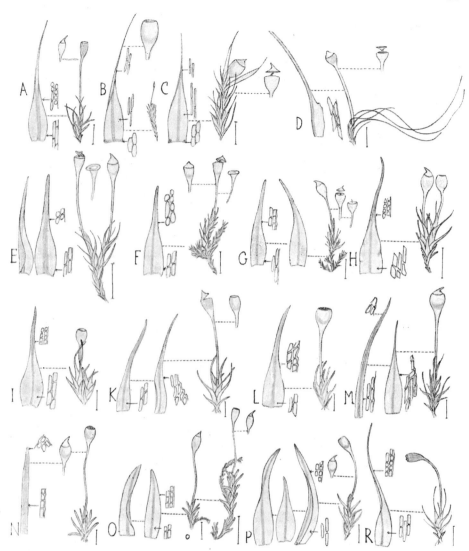

Fig. 11 A *Brachydontium trichodes*, B *Blindia acuta*, C *Stylostegium caespiticium*, D *Seligeria carniolica*, E *S. oelandica*, F *S. lapponica*, G *S. tristichoides*, H *S. polaris*, I *S. subimmersa*, K *S. doniana*, L *S. calcarea*, M *S. pusilla*, N *S. brevifolia*, O *S. diversifolia*, o var. *brevifolia*, P *S. campylopoda*, R *S. recurvata*.

angular, upper cells shortly rectangular or quadrate. Seta thick, reddish yellow; capsule globular, campanulate when empty and dry; lid united with the columella which lengthens after the ripening of the spores, finally both falling away together; peristome purple, like that of the preceding species. Spores 20—27 μ, yellowish brown, finely papillose, mature in summer. — In

compact, lime-encrusted tufts or mats, from a few mm to 1 cm high, on wet
limestone rocks.

Very rare. **S.** *Öl.* (Endemic). This species should be regarded as an isolated
form of the next species.

3. S. lapponica Nyman et Uggla in Sv. Bot. Tidskr., 1950. — Fig. 11 F
     and 12 A.

Very closely allied to the preceding species, the leaves and the capsule
are about the same, however the spores are larger, 27—31 μ, finely warty,
brownish green, mature in summer. — Tufts from a few mm to 1 cm high,
on wet calciferous rocks.

Rare, arctic-alpine species. **S.** *TL.* (Greenland).

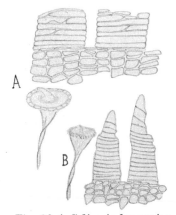

Fig. 12 A *Seligeria lapponica*,
   B *S. tristichoides*.

4. S. tristichoides Kindb. in Rev. Br.,
     1896. — Fig. 11 G. and 12 B.

Leaves in three ranks, larger towards the
stem apex, from a lanceolate base narrowing
to a stout, rough awn; nerve in the upper
part of the leaf broad, excurrent or percurrent; cells at base elongate, rectangular,
shorter in the apical part. Capsule hemispherical after the fall of the lid, without
neck; peristome reddish, teeth lanceolate,
obtuse. Spores 18—21 μ, finely papillose,
brownish, mature in summer. — In dark
green tufts on shaded, damp calcareous rocks.

Rare. **S.** *PL., TL.* **N.** *VFld., Tel., Opl., Trs.*
F. *Ks.* (North Europe, Pyrenees, Caucasus,
North America).

Var. **patula** (Lindb.) Broth., Laubm. Fennosk., 1923; (*S. trifaria* var. *patula*
Lindb. in Öfv. K. V. A. Förh., 1864). Leaves longer than the type, more spreading,
somewhat recurved. Capsule larger and with a distinct neck; exothecial cells larger.
Spores 18—20 μ. Is somewhat taller and the tufts are lighter green than those
of the type. — **S.** *Gtl.* **N.**?

5. S. polaris Berggr. in K. V. A. Handl., 1875; (*Blindia polaris* Hag. in
     K. N. V. Selsk. Skr., 1910). — Fig. 11 H.

Leaves from lanceolate base rapidly narrowed to a long awn; nerve above
broad and longly excurrent, filling up the greater part of the awn; cells in the
upper part of the leaves quadrate, in the lower part elongate, rectangular;
at angles quadrate, slightly hyaline or brownish. Seta 2—3 mm long, somewhat curved; capsule light-brown, nearly globular, reaching above the perichaetial leaves; peristome teeth reddish, lanceolate, undivided, when dry
spreading out. Spores 13—15 μ, nearly smooth, mature in summer. — In
dark-green, rigid, *Blindia*-like tufts, ½ to 2 cm high, in shaded rock crevices.

Rare arctic species. **S.** *TL.* **N.** *Fnm.* **F.** *Le.* (Spitzbergen, arctic North America).

6. S. subimmersa Lindb., Musci Scand., 1879; (*Blindia subimmersa* Hag. in K. N. V. Selsk. Skr., 1910). — Fig. 11 I.

Close to the preceding species but somewhat more slender. Leaves shorter and more erect, otherwise similar to *S. polaris*. Capsule rounded-elliptical, partially immersed in the perichaetial leaves; seta to 1½ mm long. Spores 9—11 μ, mature in summer. — In dark-green, dense cushions, to 1 cm high, on rather dry cliffs.

Very rare. **F.** *Ks.* (Endemic).

7. S. doniana (Sm.) C. Müll., Syn. Musc., 1848; (*Gymnostomum Donianum* Sm., Engl. Bot., 1806; *Anodus Donianus* Br. Eur., 1848). — Fig. 11 K.

Leaves from lanceolate, finely toothed base, gradually narrowed to a long awn; nerve ending in the apex or shortly excurrent, occupying most of the subula; cells at the leaf base rectangular to rhomboidal, in the upper part of the leaf shorter. Capsule ovoid or pyriform, hemispherical after the fall of the lid; peristome absent. — Minute, scattered plants, on stones (preferably calcareous) in damp, shaded habitats.

Scattered localities. **S.** *Vg.—TL., Öl., Gtl.* **N.** *Akh., Tel., Hord.—Trs.* **F.** *Kl., Kb., Ks.* (Europe, Asia, North America).

8. S. calcarea (Hedw.) Br. Eur., 1846; (*Weisia calcarea* Hedw., Sp. Musc., 1801; *S. crassinervis* Lindb. in Not. Sällsk. F. Fl. Fenn., 1868). — Fig. 11 L.

Leaves from ovoid, convex base rapidly narrowed to an obtuse awn; nerve becoming thicker in the upper part of the leaf and filling the awn; cells in the lower part of the leaf rectangular, transparent, in the upper part cells shortly rectangular, chlorophyllose. Seta erect, thick, yellowish; capsule pyriform, exothecial cells incrassate, irregular; peristome teeth yellowish red, short, obtuse. Spores 14—18 μ, mature in spring. — Gregarious or scattered, on calcareous rocks.

Very rare. **S.** *Vg.* **D.** *Sj., Mö.* (Europe).

9. S. pusilla (Hedw.) Br. Eur., 1846; (*Weisia pusilla* Hedw., Sp. Musc., 1801). — Fig. 11 M.

Leaves subulate from narrowly lanceolate base, margins finely denticulate; nerve thin, ending in the apex; cells in the whole leaf rectangular, thin-walled. Seta rather thick, up to 3 mm long; capsule obovoid—pyriform, exothecial cells incrassate, irregular; peristome teeth 0.10 mm, yellowish, smooth, acuminate. Spores 10—14 μ, mature in early summer. — Forming loose, dark-green, glossy tufts on damp, shaded calcareous rocks.

Rare. **S.** *Vg.* **N.** *Busk.* (Europe, Asia, North America).

The length and breadth of the leaves somewhat variable: var. **acutifolia** (Lindb.) Schimp., has broader and more rapidly narrowed leaves with a long subulate apex formed almost entirely of the nerve. Seta about 1 mm long; peristome teeth nearly obtuse. — **S.** *Gtl.* **N.** *VAgd., Möre.* (England, Italy).

10. S. brevifolia (Lindb.) Lindb. in K. V. A. Handl., 1890; (*S. pusilla* var. *brevifolia* Lindb. in Öfv. K. V. A. Förh., 1864). — Fig. 11 N.

Leaves linear, obtuse, margins finely crenulate; nerve broad but thin, ending below the apex; cells in the whole leaf homogeneous, quadrate or shortly rectangular. Capsule ovoid, erect, yellowish, exothecial cells incrassate, rectangular; peristome teeth 0,18 mm long, when dry revolute. Spores about 10 μ, mature in summer. — Minute, scattered, on vertical, shaded, calcareous or slate rocks.

Rare. **S.** *Dls., Jmt., LyL., TL.* **N.** *Hord.—Nrdl.* **F.** *Ks.* (North and Central Europe, Siberia).

11.   S. diversifolia Lindb. in Öfv. K. V. A. Förh., 1861. — Fig. 11 O.

Leaves lanceolate, entire, shortly and obtusely pointed; nerve of uniform breadth, well differentiated, ending just below the apex; cells in the whole leaf homogeneous, quadrate to shortly rectangular, at the base of the leaf somewhat longer; perichaetial leaves with long sheathing base rapidly narrowed to a short, obtuse point. Seta slightly curved, up to 4 mm long; capsule erect, ovoid, yellowish, peristome teeth obtuse; lid with an oblique beak. Spores about 10 μ, mature in summer. — In dark-green mats on damp, shaded, calcareous rocks.

Rare. **S.** *Vstm.* **N.** *Busk.* **F.** with var. *brevifolia Kl.—Ks.* (Europe, Caucasus, North America).

Var. **brevifolia** (Zett.) Hag.; (*S. recurvata* var. *brevifolia* Zett.; *S. erecta* Philib.; *S. arctica* Kaur.) — Fig. 11. O, o. — Perichaetial leaves like the apical leaves. Capsule dark, the beak of the lid short, erect. **S.** *LyL.* — **TL.** **N.** *SoFj., Opl.—Trs.* **F.** see type.

12.   S. campylopoda Kindb., Macoun., Cat. Can. Pl., 1892. — Tab. 11 P.

Leaves lanceolate, shortly, more or less obtusely pointed; nerve rather thin, percurrent or ending below the apex; cells incrassate, in the upper part of the leaf quadrate to shortly rectangular, towards the base elongate, somewhat lighter. Seta recurved when moist; capsule ovoid, exothecial cells irregularly rectangular; peristome red. Spores about 10 μ, mature in autumn. — Gregarious on damp, shaded rocks.

Rare. **S.** *Jmt.—TL.* **N.** *Akh.* **F.** *Kl., Kb., Ok.* (North Europe, North America). Like the following species but the leaves are shorter, the nerve is not excurrent and the exothecial cells are shorter and more irregular.

13.   S. recurvata (Hedw.) Br. Eur., 1846; (*Grimmia recurvata* Hedw., Sp. Musc., 1801; *S. setacea* Lindb. in Öfv. K. V. A. Förh., 1863; *S. paludosa* Hag. in K. N. V. Selsk. Skr., 1910). — Fig. 11 R.

Leaves narrowly lanceolate with a long, fine, somewhat curved, entire subula; nerve excurrent, forming the upper part of the subula; cells in the upper part of the leaf shortly rectangular or quadrate, incrassate, becoming more elongate and pellucid towards the base of the leaf. Seta arcuate when moist; capsule ovoid, when empty and dry slightly furrowed, exothecial cells longly rectangular; peristome brownish red. Spores about 10 μ, mature in spring and early summer. — Gregarious on shaded, damp sandstone or slightly calcareous rocks.

Isolated localities. **S.** *Sk.—TL., Gtl.* **N.** *Akh.—Fnm.* **F.** *Al.* (Europe, North America).

14. Brachydontium Bruch, Fürnr. in Flora, 1827.

In habit like a *Seligeria* but is distinguished from the other genus of *Seligeriaceae* by the striate capsule, the presence of a large annulus, papillose peristome teeth, and a 5-cleft, mitriform calyptra.

49. B. trichodes (Web. f.) Bruch, Fürnr. in Flora, 1827; (*Gymnostomum trichodes* Web. f. in Web. et Mohr, Ind. Musc. Pl. Crypt., 1803). — Fig. 11 A.

Leaves from narrowly ovate base, rapidly narrowed to a long, fine subula; nerve rather strong, filling the subula; cells in the upper part of the leaf small, opaque, quadrate, in the lower part longly rectangular, colourless. Seta 2—3 mm long, yellowish, rather thick; capsule erect, oval, striated; peristome papillose, pale, and short, not reaching above the annulus. Spores about 10 µ, smooth, mature in autumn. — Forms shining tufts, about 1 mm high, on damp, shady, siliceous walls and boulders in the upper part of the woodland region to the snow line.

Isolated localities. **N.** *Busk.*, *Rog.*, *Hord.*, *SoFj.*, *Möre*. (North, West, and Central Europe, North America).

Fam. V. Dicranaceae

Autoicous or dioicous. Stem leaves nearly equal in length, erect, erecto-patent, sometimes falcate, usually narrowly or broadly lanceolate, leaf base more or less sheathing; nerve broad or narrow, excurrent or percurrent, seldom ending below the apex; cells smooth, more seldom mamillose or papillose, in the lower part of the leaf usually elongate and often porose, in the upper part cells shorter, sometimes quadrate, angular cells not or well-differentiated. Capsule inclined or erect, with or without stomata and annulus; peristome single, teeth 16, more or less deeply divided, rarely entire, in the upper part usually papillose, in the lower part vertically point-striated, rarely papillose or irregularly striated to nearly smooth; lid usually rostrate; calyptra cucullate. Stem usually with central strand. — Large to very small mosses usually growing in mats on soil or rocks preferably in the temperate zones, the genus *Campylopus* however principally in the tropics.

I   Angular cells not or only slightly differentiated (except
    Oncophorus virens and *Dicranoweisia crispula*), upper cells
    sometimes papillose or mamillose; the leaf recurved, plane
    or incurved
    1 Cells in the upper part of the leaf mostly elongate, pa-
      renchymatous or prosenchymatous
      a Cleistocarpous; seta very short .... 15. *Pseudephemerum*
      aa Stegocarpous; seta long
        b Leaves erect, appressed to the stem; androecium
          disc-shaped .... 16. *Aongstroemia*
        bb Leaves erect-spreading, flexuose or squarrose;
          androecium bud-shaped .... 17. *Dicranella*
    2 Cells in the upper part of the leaf mostly quadrate
      a Leaves linear-lanceolate or linear-oblong, acute or
        obtuse

b Cells in the upper part of the leaf mamillose or
  papillose
  c Capsule not striate
    d Dioicous; leaves patent or squarrose; capsule
      mostly inclined ....18. *Dichodontium*
    dd Autoicous; leaves erecto-patent;
      capsule erect .... 19. *Oreoweisia*
  cc Capsule striate ....21. *Cnestrum*
  bb Leaf cells not mamillose but with numerous mi-
    nute cuticle-papillae; capsule with 8 strong striae .....20. *Rhabdoweisia*
aa Leaves from a lanceolate base narrowed to a ± long
  apex
  b Cells in the upper part of the leaf mostly papillose;
    capsule more or less striate; (*Cynodontium bruntonii*
    has a smooth capsule)
    c Androecium on a short stalk, — fig. 20 B, ♂; —
      small species on ± calciferous rocks ....21. *Cnestrum*
    cc Androecium without stalk, — fig. 21 D and F, ♂;
      — larger species on siliceous rocks ....22. *Cynodontium*
  bb Cells mostly smooth in the upper part of the leaf;
    capsule not striate
    c Leaves spreading or recurved; capsule curved and
      inclined; peristome teeth in the lower part finely
      vertically point-striated...........................23. *Oncophorus*
    cc Leaves erect-spreading; capsule symmetrical,
      erect; peristome teeth nearly smooth, papillose or
      shortly and irregularly point-striated ....24. *Dicranoweisia*
II Angular cells differentiated (except *Leucobryum*, some
  species of *Campylopus* and *Metzlerella* have very fragile
  basal cells), enlarged, thin-walled, upper cells smooth,
  seldom slightly papillose; leaf margin plane or incurved
  1 Nerve thin or strong (in cross section convex, without
    thin-walled hyaline cells); lamina cells homogeneous
    from the nerve to the margin
    a Autoicous; androecium bud-shaped, below the peri-
      chaetium; leaves usually without stereids
    b Seta thick and short; capsule broadly oval ....25. *Arctoa*
    bb Seta thinner and longer; capsule oval to cylindrical,
      ± curved and inclined ....26. *Kiaeria*
    aa Dioicous; leaves usually with stereids
    b Angular cells mostly bistratose, the cells above the
      basal cells towards the nerve enlarged and hyaline.......27. *Dicranum*
    bb Angular cells mostly unistratose, all cells around
      the basal cells homogeneous.....................28. *Orthodicranum*
  2 Nerve broad and flattened, often occupying the greater
    part of the leaf (with or without hyaline cells); lamina
    cells decreasing in size from the nerve to the margins
    a Nerve without median chlorophyllose cells
    b Cells in the upper part of the leaf and at the margins
      narrow and thin-walled; peristome teeth divided or
      perforated almost to the base
      c Autoicous; seta erect; calyptra longer than the
        capsule ....29. *Metzlerella*
      cc Dioicous; seta arcuate before the spores are ma-
        ture; calyptra shorter than the capsule ....30. *Dicranodontium*
    bb Cells in the upper part of the leaf quadrate or
      rhomboidal to linear, vermicular; peristome teeth
      divided to about the middle ....31. *Campylopus*
    aa Transverse section of nerve with central chlorophyllose
      cells surrounded on both sides by hyaline cells

15. Pseudephemerum (Lindb.) Hag. in K. N. V. Selsk. Skr., 1910; (*Pleuridium Pseudephemerum* Lindb. in Öfv. K. V. A. Förh., 1864).

Synoicous, cleistocarpous. Antheridia naked in the axils of the perichaetial leaves. Leaves lanceolate, smooth, margin plane, at the lower part of the stem small, larger towards the stem apex, apical and perichaetial leaves similar; nerve thin, ending below the apex. Capsule on a very short seta, immersed in the perichaetial leaves.

1. P. nitidum (Hedw.) C. Jens.,
Skand. Bladmossfl., 1939; (*Phascum nitidum* Hedw., Sp. Musc.,
1801; *Pleuridium axillare* Lindb.,
Öfv. K. V. A. Förh., 1864). —
Fig. 13.

Leaves lanceolate, concave, in the upper part finely serrulate; areolation pellucid, cells rectangular, thin-walled. Capsule oval, shortly pointed, pale brown. Spores 24—30 μ, yellow, papillose, mature late summer to autumn. — In loose, green to pale green mats on muddy soil.

Fig. 13 *Pseudephemerum nitidum.*

Not uncommon in the lowlands. **S.** *Sk.—Gstr.* **N.** *ÖFld.—Hord.* **F.** *Al., Ab., Nyl., Ka., Oa.* **D.** *Jl., Fy., Sj.* (Europe, Azores, Algeria, Morocco, the volcanoes in Central Africa).

16. Aongstroemia Br. Eur., 1846.

Dioicous. Androecia disc-shaped, antheridia and paraphyses numerous. Stem simple or with occasional, rigid, erect branches. Leaves erect, appressed. Capsule symmetrical, erect or slightly incurved; peristome teeth entire or divided to the middle.

1. A. longipes (Sommerf.) Br. Eur., 1846; (*Weisia longipes* Sommerf. in Suppl. ad Wg., Fl. Lapp. 1826). — Fig. 14.

Lower stem leaves broad, short, ± obtuse, few denticulations at the apex, upper or perichaetial leaves larger and ± acuminate; nerve thin, ending below the apex; cells smooth, elongate or rhomboidal, narrower at the margin. Seta red; capsule oval,

Fig. 14 *Aongstroemia longipes.*

smooth, brown, exothecial cells elongate, incrassate; peristome in the lower part brown-red, finely point-striated to smooth, the apex of the teeth yellow, finely striate, papillose. Spores 15—20 µ, mature in summer. — About 5 mm high, forming loose mats on damp, sandy soil in the coniferous forest and subalpine wood regions of the mountains.

Rare. **S.** *Vg., Dlr., Hjd.—TL.* **N.** *Opl., Hdm., STrd.—Fnm.* **F.** *Ka.—Ks.* (Iceland, Alps, Yenisei, North America, Greenland).

Var. **sericea** Hag. in Tromsö Mus. Aarsh., 1899—1901. Tufts a few cm high, dark green, glossy. Only sterile plants known. — **N.** *Nrdl.*

17. **Dicranella** Schimp., Br. Eur. Coroll., 1855; (*Anisothecium* Mitt. in Journ. Linn. Soc. Bot., 1869).

Mostly dioicous. Leaves from ± sheathing base abruptly subulate or gradually narrowed (*D. squarrosa* with obtuse apex); nerve broad or narrow, in cross section with the dorsal stereid band well developed, the ventral band absent or with few stereids — fig. 15 B, xn, K, xn and 16 xl; — cells mostly smooth, rectangular or linear, without differentiated angular cells. Capsule on a red or yellow seta, erect and symmetrical or curved and asymmetrical; exothecial cells usually incrassate; annulus large or absent; peristome purple, brownish red or yellowish brown, teeth divided to about the middle, in upper part papillose, in the lower part finely vertically point-striated, basal membrane short. — Mostly small species on soil.

I Stem leaves squarrose, the base mostly sheathing; — fig. 15 A—D
    1 Leaves broadly obtuse .... 1. *D. squarrosa*
    2 Leaves acute or subulate
      a Capsule curved, asymmetrical
        b Capsule smooth .... 2. *D. schreberi*
        bb Capsule striate .... 3. *D. grevilleana*
      aa Capsule erect, symmetrical, striate .... 4. *D. crispa*
II Stem leaves erect, flexuose or falcate — fig. 15 E—K, 16
    1 Seta red; nerve occupying 1/5 of the leaf base
      a Margin of leaf recurved; exothecial cells with thickened longitudinal and thin transverse walls .... 5. *D. varia*
      aa Margin of leaf plane; exothecial cells with uniformly thickened walls
        b Apical and perichaetial leaves like the stem leaves
          c Capsule without struma
            d Capsule asymmetrical, curved .... 6. *D. rigidula*
            dd Capsule symmetrical, erect .... 7. *D. rufescens*
          cc Capsule with struma .... 8. *D. riparia*
        bb Apical and perichaetial leaves from sheathing base often ± squarrose .... 9. *D. subulata*
    2 Seta yellow; nerve about 1/3 of the leaf base
      a Leaf margin entire or indistinctly serrulate; capsule with struma .... 10. *D. cerviculata*
      aa Leaf margin distinctly serrulate; capsule without struma .... 11. *D. heteromalla*

1. **D. squarrosa** (Starke) Schimp., Syn. Musc. Eur., 1860; (*Dicranum squarrosum* Starke, Schrad. in Journ. Bot., 1801; *Anisothecium squarrosum* Lindb., Utkast, 1878). — Fig. 15 A.

Dioicous. Leaves from broad, sheathing base oblong-lanceolate, squarrose, apex obtuse, concave, slightly crenulate; nerve thin, ending below the apex; cells thin-walled, broadly rhomboidal, hexagonal, rectangular, in the upper part of the leaf slightly mamillose. Seta red; capsule smooth, slightly curved; annulus absent; peristome teeth brown-red to purple, with a fine vertical point-striation below, yellow and papillose upwards; basal membrane 4 or 5 cells wide. Spores 18—20 µ, yellowish, finely papillose, mature in autumn. — Robust species in loose yellow-green cushions beside streams, in springs, etc.

A not uncommon subalpine species. **S., N.** Rare or scattered in the southern provinces, more common in the north. **F.** *Al., Ok., Li.* **D.** *Jl., Sj.* (Europe, Caucasus North America).

2. **D. schreberi** (Hedw.) Schimp., Br. Eur. Coroll., 1855; (*Dicranum Schreberianum* Hedw., Sp. Musc., 1801; *Anisothecium crispum* Lindb., Utkast, 1878; *Anisothecium Schreberianum* Dix. in Rev. Bryol. N. S., 1933). — Fig. 15 B.

Dioicous. Leaves from sheathing base lanceolate, more or less subulate, squarrose, serrulate above; nerve thin, ending in or below the apex, serrulate at back of the subula; cells mostly rectangular. Seta red; capsule smooth, more or less curved and asymmetrical, exothecial cells regularly rectangular, longitudinal walls thickened, transverse walls thinner (comp. *D. varia*, fig. 15 E); annulus absent; peristome finely point-striated below, diagonally striated and hardly papillose above. Spores about 16—18 µ, yellow, finely papillose, mature in autumn. — In green to yellowish green, loose tufts, ½ to 2 cm high on damp, loamy or sandy earth.

Scattered. **S. N. F.** throughout the country but most common in the northern and central provinces (*Öl., Gtl.* O), **D.** *Jl., Fy., Sj. Brnh.* (Europe, Asia, North America, New Zealand).

Var. **elata** Schimp., Syn. 2., 1876; (*Dicranella lenta* Wils., Msc., Braithw. in Journ. of Bot., 1871). — Fig. 15 B, b. — Is a larger form found in wetter places. The leaves are more gradually narrowed than those of the type; the cells are wider. Capsule short, symmetrical. In habit like a small form of *D. squarrosa*. Extreme forms are very unlike the type but different intermediate forms are common. Perhaps the whole series are only habitat modifications of the type.

3. **D. grevilleana** (Brid.) Schimp., Br. Eur. Coroll., 1855; (*Dicranum Schreberi* var. *Grevilleanum* Brid., Br. Univ., 1826; *Dicranum Grevilleanum* Br. Eur., 1847; *Anisothecium Grevilleanum* Lindb., Utkast, 1878). — Fig. 15 C.

Dioicous or autoicous. Leaves from sheathing base lanceolate, subulate, squarrose; nerve thin, usually smooth, ending in the apex; cells rectangular. Seta red, capsule faintly striate when dry, more or less curved, sometimes slightly strumose, exothecial cells incrassate, parenchymatous or prosenchymatous; annulus absent; peristome finely point-striated below, finely papillose above. Spores about 17 µ, finely papillose, mature in autumn. — Tufts usually 1—2 cm high, yellowish green. Found on damp, loamy soils.

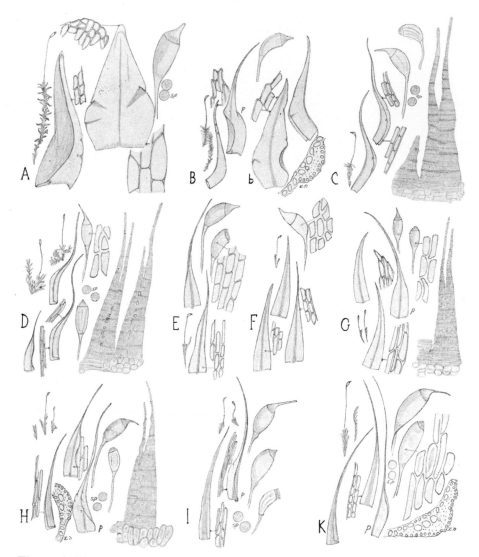

Fig. 15 A *Dicranella squarrosa*,   B *D. schreberi*,   b var. *elata*,   C *D. grevilleana*,
D *D. crispa*,   E *D. varia*,   F *D. rigidula*,   G *D. rufescens*,   H *D. subulata*,   I *D. cerviculata*,   K *D. heteromalla*.

Scattered in subalpine region. **S.** *Vg.*, *Vstm.*, *Gstr.*—*TL.* **N.** *Akh.*—*Fnm.* **F.** *Al.*, *Ta.*—*Lps.* (Europe, Asia, North America).

Like the preceding species, but more often with capsules and then easily recognized by the striate capsule with irregular exothecial cells. Large and barren forms can be very difficult to determine. *D. grevilleana* has longer and somewhat more rapidly narrowed leaves than *D. schreberi*. The nerve is usually smooth.

4. D. crispa (Hedw.) Schimp., Br. Eur. Coroll., 1855; (*Dicranum crispum* Hedw., Sp. Musc., 1801; *Anisothecium vaginale* Loeske, Studien, 1910). — Fig. 15 D.

Dioicous or autoicous. Leaves from sheathing base quickly narrowed to a long, squarrose or flexuose subula; nerve thin; cells narrowly rectangular. Seta red. Capsule erect, striate; exothecial cells mostly rectangular, incrassate; peristome below brown-red or brownish yellow, vertically point-striated, above the teeth are yellow and papillose; basal membrane of 2 rows of cells; annulus of large cells. Spores $17-20$ μ, greenish, finely papillose, nearly smooth, mature in late summer. — A small species in loose tufts on sandy or loamy soil.

Rare or scattered in the southern provinces, more common in the north. **S. N. F.** in the whole area, but in mountains hardly above the wood limit. **D.** rare. *Jl.*, *Fy.*, *Sj.*, *Brnh.* (North, West, and Central Europe, North Asia, North America). Easily recognized by the narrow, erect, striate capsule.

5. D. varia (Hedw.) Schimp., Br. Eur. Coroll., 1855; (*Dicranum varium* Hedw., Sp. Musc., 1801; *Aongstroemia varia* C. Müll., Syn. I., 1849; *Anisothecium varium* Mitt. in Journ. Linn. Soc. Bot., 1869; *Anisothecium rubrum* Lindb., Utkast, 1878). — Fig. 15 E.

Dioicous. Leaves rigid, erecto-patent, narrowly lanceolate, margin narrowly recurved below; nerve strong, excurrent; cells in the upper part of the leaf narrow-lanceolate, partially bistratose, towards the base cells enlarged. Seta red; capsule smooth, inclined, and curved; exothecial cells rectangular, with thickened longitudinal walls, transverse walls thin; annulus absent; peristome brown-red, with basal membrane of 4 rows of cells. Spores brownish, $15-17$ μ, mature in winter. — Bright or yellowish green tufts, up to 2 cm high, on damp, loamy soil.

Not uncommon in the lowlands, very rare above forest reg. **S., N., F., D.** in most provinces. (Europe, Azores, Madeira, Canaries, Asia, North Africa, North America).

Var. **callistomum** (Turn.) Br. Eur., (*Dicranum callistomum* Turn., Musc. Hib.). Seta shorter; capsule smaller and more erect than that of the type; lid almost as large as the capsule. Occurs mixed together with the type.

6. D. rigidula (Hedw.) Dix. in Rev. Bryol. N. S., 1933; (*Dicranum rigidulum* Hedw., Sp. Musc., 1801; *D. humilis* Ruthe in Hedwigia, 1873; *Anisothecium humile* Lindb., Utkast, 1878). — Fig. 15 F.

Dioicous. Leaves narrow-lanceoalate, margins plane; apical leaves linear-lanceolate, ± secund; nerve thin; cells rectangular, thin-walled, unistratose in the whole leaf. Seta red; capsule slightly curved, exothecial cells irregular, incrassate; annulus absent; lid long, conical, ½ the length of the capsule; peristome brown-red; basal membrane of 4 rows of cells. Spores yellowish, $14-17$ μ, mature in autumn. — Gregarious or in loose tufts on damp, sandy or loamy soil.

Rare. **S.** *Bl.*, *Vg.*, *Dls.*, *Vrm.*, *Jmt.*, *Ång.* **N.** *ÖFld.*, *Akh.*, *Busk.*, *Nrdl.*, *Trs.* **F.** *Al.*, *Ab.*, *Ik.*, *St.*, *Sa.*, *Ta.*, *Tb.*, *Sb.*, *Ok.*, *Ks.* (Europe, Siberia, North America?).

7. D. rufescens (Sm.) Schimp., Br. Eur. Coroll., 1855; (*Dicranum rufescens* Sm., Engl. Bot., 1804; *Aongstroemia rufescens* C. Müll., Syn. I., 1849; *Anisothecium rufescens* Lindb., Utkast, 1878). — Fig. 15 G.

Dioicous. Leaves lanceolate, gradually narrowed, mostly secund; nerve thin, ending in or below the apex; areolation lax; cells rectangular, with thin walls. Seta red; capsule erect, oval, exothecial cells irregular and incrassate; annulus absent; peristome brown-red, below with coarse vertical point-striation, above teeth yellowish, and somewhat coarsely papillose, basal membrane of approx. 10 rows of cells. Spores about 14 μ, finely and sparsely papillose, greenish, mature in winter. — Small, reddish-brown plants, gregarious or in loose mats on damp, sandy or loamy soil.

Scattered in the lowlands. **S.** *Sk.* — *Vb.* **N.** *ÖFld.* — *Nrdl.* **F.** the southern provinces to *Ok.*, **D.** *Jl.*, *Sj.* (Europe, Madeira, Asia, North America, Costa Rica).

Fig. 16 *Dicranella riparia.*

8. D. riparia (Lindb., ex. Lindb.) Mårt. et Nyh. in Bot. Not., 1954; (*Oncophorus riparius* H. Lindb. in Medd. Soc. F. Fl. Fenn.,1900; *Oncophorus Hambergii* Arn. et Jens., Moose Sarekg., 1910; *Kiaeria Starkei* var. *riparia* Hag. in K. N. V. Selsk. Skr., 1914; *Dicranum Blyttii* var. *riparium* C. Jens., Skand. Bladmossfl., 1939). — Fig. 16.

Autoicous. Androecium bud-like, in leaf-axils just below the perichaetium. Stem leaves lanceolate, erecto-patent; nerve flat, occupying the greater part of the apex, slightly mamillose in the upper part at back; cells polymorphous, elongate — quadrate — triangular. Seta below reddish, above yellowish, when old dark-reddish; capsule curved, strumose, plicate when dry and empty; exothecial cells hexagonal to rectangular; annulus of (1—)2 rows of large cells; peristome reddish-brown. Lid rostrate. Spores yellowish green, smooth, 15—20 μ. — In compact tufts or mats a few cm high on sandy ground beside streams.

Rare. **S.** *LL.*, *TL.* **N.** *Opl.* **F.** *Ik.* (Known only from Fennoscandia).

9. D. subulata (Hedw.) Schimp., Br. Eur. Coroll, 1855; (*Dicranum subulatum* Hedw., Sp. Musc., 1801; *D. secunda* Sw., 1795; Lindb., Musci Scand., 1879). — Fig. 15 H.

Dioicous. Lower leaves from lanceolate base longly subulate, flexuose, with channelled apex; apical, perichaetial, and perigonial leaves rapidly narrowed from oval, sheathing base; nerve thin, excurrent; cells elongate, rectangular. Seta red; capsule more or less curved, symmetrical or asymmetrical, slightly striate, plicate when dry and empty; exothecial cells irregular, mostly prosenchymatous, with thick walls; annulus of large cells; peristome yellowish brown, with a very fine vertical point-striation below, teeth in the upper part finely papillose; lid subulate-rostrate. Spores about 18 μ, green-brown, very finely papillose, mature in autumn or winter. — In low, loose, somewhat glossy mats on damp, sandy or loamy soil, from the lowlands to the low alpine belt of the mountains.

Rare in the South, frequent in the North. **S. N. F.** in most provinces. **D.** *Jl.*, *Brnh.* (North and Central Europe, Asia, North America, Greenland).

Var. **curvata** (Hedw.) Schimp., Br. Eur. Coroll., 1855; (*Dicranum curvatum* Hedw., Sp. Musc., 1801). Capsule symmetrical, nearly erect. Mostly scattered plants together with the type. Is perhaps only a poorly developed form of the type.

10. D. cerviculata (Hedw.) Schimp., Br. Eur. Coroll., 1855; (*Dicranum cerviculatum* Hedw., Sp. Musc., 1801). — Fig. 15 I.

Dioicous. Lower leaves slightly falcate, narrowly lanceolate; apical and perichaetial leaves falcate or falcato-secund, from sheathing base, abruptly narrowed to a long, channelled subula, entire or serrulate above; nerve very broad, ½ to ⅓ the width of the leaf base; cells rectangular or elongate. Seta yellow; capsule broadly oval, slightly curved, with struma; exothecial cells mostly prosenchymatous, thin-walled; annulus a single, differentiated row of cells; peristome like that of the preceding species. Spores 17 to more than 20 μ, yellowish brown, nearly smooth, mature in late summer. — In green, yellowish green, often wide mats in turf cuttings, on damp humus, seldom on loamy or sandy soil, from the lowlands to high in the mountains.

Common in suitable habitats in the whole territory. **S. N. F. D.** (Europe, Asia to Sakhalin, North America, Greenland, Costa Rica).

Easily recognized by the short, curved, and strumose capsule. Tall, sterile tufts may be confused with *D. heteromalla*, but the latter has the leaf margin distinctly serrulate towards the middle. *D. cerviculata* has entire or indistinctly serrulate leaf margins.

11 D. heteromalla (Hedw.) Schimp., Br. Eur. Coroll., 1855; (*Dicranum heteromallum* Hedw., Sp. Musc., 1801; *Aongstroemia heteromalla* C. Müll., Syn. I., 1849). — Fig. 15 K.

Dioicous. Leaves erecto-patent or falcato-secund, narrowly lanceolate, finely subulate, margin serrulate from middle upwards; perichaetial leaves rapidly narrowed from broad sheathing base; nerve broad, about ⅓ the width of the leaf base; cells rectangular, above shorter. Seta yellow, when old often dark-reddish; capsule oval, slightly curved, smooth, sulcate when empty and dry; exothecial cells prosenchymatous, slightly incrassate; annulus poorly differentiated; peristome brown-red, like that of the preceding species. Spores 14—15 μ, finely papillose, nearly smooth, mature in winter. — In soft, glossy, green or yellowish green mats 1—3 cm high, on sandy humus, road-sides, etc.

Common in the southern provinces. **S.** *Sk.—Dlr.* **N.** *ÖFld.—Nrdl.* **F.** the southern part to *Ob.* **D.** throughout the country. (Europe, Asia, Madeira, Canaries, North America).

A variable species regarding the length and direction of the leaves. Forma **interrupta** (Hedw.) Br. Eur. Is a large form. Leaves falcato-secund, at apex crowded and longer. — Forma **sericea** (Schimp.) Mönkem. Leaves erecto-patent or slightly secund, with long, serrulate apex. Tufts yellowish green, glossy. — Forma **stricta** Br. Eur. Leaves erect-spreading, rather rigid.

18. **Dichodontium** Schimp., Br. Eur. Coroll., 1855.

Dioicous. Leaves from erect, broad base, lanceolate or lingulate, patent or squarrose; nerve strong, ending below the apex, in cross section with stereids; cells beside the nerve at the base of the leaf elongate, smooth, towards the margin and in the upper part of the leaf rounded-quadrate, mamillose. Capsule ovoid or oblong, more or less inclined; annulus and struma lacking. Stem with central strand.

Fig. 17 *Dichodontium pellucidum.*

1. **D. pellucidum** (Hedw.) Schimp., Br. Eur. Coroll., 1855; (*Dicranum pellucidum* Hedw., Sp. Musc., 1801; *Dicranum flavescens* Turn., Musc. Hib., 1804; *D. flavescens* Lindb. in Bot. Not., 1878). — Fig. 17.

Leaves soft, margins more or less serrulate; perichaetial leaves like the stem leaves. Seta yellow; capsule curved or symmetrical, inclined or more seldom erect; exothecial cells with very thick longitudinal walls but thin transverse walls; peristome brown-red, with fine vertical point-striation, at apex yellowish and papillose, basal membrane 6—7 rows of cells. Spores 14—17 μ, yellow, slightly papillose, mature in autumn or in winter. — Loose, dark- or light-green soft tufts, 2—8 cm high, on wet soil, beside lakes, on rocks in or near streams, especially where lime is present.

Rather common in suitable localities from the lowlands to high in the mountains. **S., N., F.** in most provinces, **D.** *Jl., Fy., Sj.* (Europe, Madeira, Asia, North America).

As regards habit a variable species. There are forms with short, nearly entire, and ± stiff leaves or with long, broad, and sharply serrulate leaves. But the species is always easily recognized by the leaves, which are ± linearly lingulate with margins more or less serrate, and by the mamillose lamina cells.

19. **Oreoweisia** DNot., Epil., 1869.

Fig. 18 *Oreoweisia serrulata.*

Autoicous. Androecium close below the gynoecium, bud-like, with 2—3 perigonial bracts. Leaves linear-lingulate, spreading from erect base; nerve strong, ending below the apex, in cross section with stereids; cells in the upper part of the leaf rounded-quadrate, pointed-mamillose, below rectangular, elongate, smooth. Capsule oval, smooth, erect or slightly inclined. Stem with central strand.

1. **O. serrulata** (Funck) DNot. Epil., 1869; (*Weisia serrulata* Funck in Brid., Br. Univ., 1826; *Cynodontium serrulatum* Jur. in Zool. — Bot. Verh., 1871). — Fig. 18.

Leaves with obtuse or acute apex, the margins in the upper part of the leaf serrulate with projecting cells. Capsule brown, exothecial cells incrassate; annulus of 2—3 rows, thin-walled, not separating cells; peristome red-brown, teeth lanceolate, undivided, very slightly striated and papillose, nearly smooth. Spores 18—24 μ, brown-red, warty. — Compact tufts, 1—4 cm high, with radicles more or less papillose. On soil in rock-crevices in alp. reg.

Very rare mountain plant. **N.** *SoFj.* (Alps, North America).

20. Rhabdoweisia Br. Eur., 1846.

Autoicous. Androecium bud-like, with a short stalk. Leaves linear-lanceolate, spreading, crisped when dry, margins mostly plane; cells in the upper part of the leaf rounded-quadrate, chlorophyllose, towards the base rectangular, pale, with thinner walls. Seta yellow; capsule broadly oval, symmetrical, strongly 8-striated, furrowed when dry and empty; annulus absent; peristome small, teeth 16, filiform or lanceolate, undivided. Stem without central strand.

I Leaves entire or slightly crenulate; peristome teeth fili-
form . . . . .1. *R. fugax*

II Margin in the upper part of the leaf irregularly toothed;
peristome teeth lanceolate . . . . .2. *R. denticulata*

1.   R. fugax (Hedw.) Br. Eur., 1846; (*Weisia fugax* Hedw., Sp. Musc., 1801; *Weisia stricta* Kaulf. in Sturm, Deutschl. Fl., 1818; *Oncophorus striatus* Lindb., Musci Scand., 1879; *R. striata* Kindb., Eur. et N. Am. Br., 1897). — Fig. 19 A.

Leaves linear-lanceolate, entire or crenulate; cells in the upper part of the leaf rounded-quadrate 8—10 μ, minute cuticle-papillae numerous and visible under the microscope; nerve mostly about 40 μ wide, ending below the apex. Seta short; capsule rounded-pyriform, striate; peristome teeth smooth, from a broad base, rapidly narrowed, filiform. Spores about 17 μ, brown, finely papillose, mature in summer. — Dense tufts, 1, rarely up to 3 cm high, radiculose below. In shaded, ± damp rock crevices, on earth-covered, shaded boulders, preferably on siliceous substrata.

Scattered, most common in the western provinces. **S., N., F.** in most provinces. **D.** *Brnh.* (Europe, Azores, Madeira, Asia, North America).

2.   R. denticulata (Brid.) Br. Eur., 1846; (*Weisia denticulata* Brid., Sp. Musc., 1811; *Weisia striata* β *major* Hook. et Tayl., Musc. Brit., 1818; *Oncophorus crispatus* Lindb., Musci Scand., 1879; *R. crispata* Kindb., Eur. et N. Am. Br., 1897). — Fig. 19 B.

Leaves like those of the preceding species, but margins in the upper part of the leaf irregularly serrate or toothed, with projecting cells; cells in the upper part of the leaf (10—)12—14 μ; nerve mostly 70—80 μ broad. Cap-

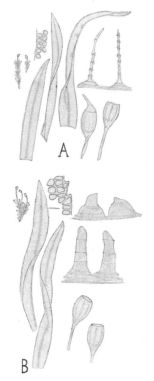

sule like that of the preceding species, but larger; peristome teeth lanceolate, gradually narrowed, finely and slightly striate, sometimes smooth, short, and less developed. Spores 19—20 μ, brown, finely papillose, mature in summer. — Like the foregoing species, but the tufts are mostly somewhat larger. Occurs in similar situations as the preceding species, but perhaps in damper places.

Scattered in the West, rare in the East. **S.** *Sk.*, *Sm.*, *Hl.*, *Vg.*, *Boh.*, *Dsl.*, *Ög.*, *Dlr.*, *LL.* **N.** common in *Vestl.*, elsewhere rare. **F.** *Al.* (Europe, North America, Hawaii).

21. Cnestrum Hag. in K. N. V. Selsk. Skr., 1914.

Autoicous. Androecium bud-like, with a short stalk inserted just below the gynoecium. Leaves linear-lanceolate, margin narrowly recurved, the upper part of the lamina with small, highly mamillose cells, below cells rectangular and smooth. Capsule rounded-oval, yellowish, striate; neck short; peristome red, teeth below point-striated, at apex papillose, when dry teeth spreading out, with the apex curved inward. — Slender mosses on earth-covered stones or in rock crevices.

Fig. 19 A *Rhabdoweisia fugax*, B *R. denticulata*.

I Leaves obtuse; the upper half of the peristome teeth divided .... 1. *C. alpestre*

II Leaves acute; peristome teeth not divided, only sometimes split at the margin........................ 2. *C. schisti*

1. C. alpestre (Wg.) Nyh. in Bot. Not., 1953.; (*Dicranum alpestre* Wg., Fl. Lapp., 1812; *Oncophorus alpestris* Lindb., Musci Scand., 1879; *Cynodontium alpestre* Lindb. in Limpr., Laubm., 1886). — Fig. 20 A.

Leaf margin finely serrulate from apex to below the middle of the leaf, with large projecting mamillae; nerve ending below the apex; cells in the upper part of the leaf quadrate, mamillose, below rectangular and smooth. Capsule erect; peristome red, teeth divided to about the middle; lid rostellate, with a long, oblique rostrum. Spores 15—20 μ, finely papillose, mature in summer. — Low, soft tufts on earth-covered stones, in rock crevices, etc., preferably on calcareous substrata.

Rare arctic-alpine species. **S.** *Jmt.*, *Nb.*, *PL.*, *LL.*, *TL.* **N.** *ÖAgd.*, *Hdm.*, *Opl.*, *STrd.*, *Trs.*, *Fnm.* **F.** *Kl.*, *Sa.*, *Om.*, *Ks.*, *Le.*, *Li.* (Kola, Yenisei, Amur, Greenland).

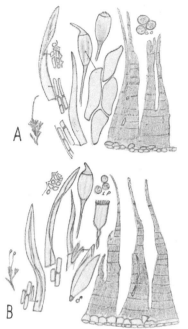

2. C. schisti (Wg.) Hag. in K. N. V. Selsk. Skr., 1914; (*Weisia schisti* Wg., Fl. Lapp., 1812; *Cynodontium Schisti* Lindb. in Öfv. K. V. A. Förh.,1864; *Oncophorus Schisti* Lindb., Musc. Scand., 1879). — Fig. 20 B.

Leaves like those of the preceding species, but acute. Capsule erect; peristome red, teeth not divided, sometimes perforated or at margin irregularly split. Spores 12—14 µ, finely papillose, mature in spring. — Low, soft, often dense tufts, growing in rock crevices, in Sweden usually on hyperite.

Scattered. **S.** most provinces from *Sm.* —*Vb.* and *LL.* (*Öl.*, *Gtl.* O) **N.** *Akh.*—*Fnm.* **F.** most provinces (*Al.* O). (Central Europe, Yenisei, Amur, North America, Ellesmere Island, Greenland).

Fig. 20 A *Cnestrum alpestre*, B *C. schisti*.

22. Cynodontium Schimp., Br. Eur. Coroll., 1855.

Autoicous. Androecium without stalk, inserted below the gynoecium, usually 2 perigonial leaves. Stem leaves erecto-patent, when dry mostly crispate, narrowly lanceolate, margin recurved in the middle of the leaf; nerve strong, percurrent or ending below the apex, rarely shortly excurrent, in cross section usually with two stereid bands; cells in the upper part of the leaf more or less mamillose, quadrate or shortly and irregularly rectangular, towards the base cells longer, enlarged, alar cells not or only slightly differentiated. Capsule regularly or slightly curved, with or without struma; when developed, peristome reddish, teeth divided, vertically point-striated below, yellow and papillose above. Stem with central strand. — Growing in tufts or mats on siliceous rocks.

I Peristome short and irregular, smooth or slightly striated ......2. *C. bruntonii*
II Peristome normally developed
  1 Annulus of large cells, separating, — fig. 21 C
    a Capsule curved, with struma ....3. *C. strumiferum*
    aa Capsule symmetrical, without struma
     b With quadrate, slightly differentiated angular cells;
      nerve shortly excurrent ....1. *C. suecicum*
     bb Angular cells not differentiated; nerve ending in or
      below the apex
      c Cells in the upper part of the leaf incrassate, irregular, 6—8 µ ....5. *C. polycarpum*
      cc Cells in the upper part of the leaf regularly quadrate, about 14 µ ....4. *C. jenneri*
  2 Annulus narrow and persistent
    a Perigonial leaf obtuse; leaf slightly mamillose..............6. *C. tenellum*

aa Perigonial leaf acute; leaf highly mamillose
  b Cells in the upper part of the leaf 7 — 8 μ; seta curved
    when moist .... 7. *C. gracilescens*
  bb Cells in the upper part of the leaf about 13 μ; seta
    erect .... 8. *C. fallax*

1.   **C. suecicum** (Arn. et Jens.) Hag. in Tromsö Mus. Aarsh., 1899; (*Oncophorus suecicus* Arn. et Jens. in Rev. Br., 1895). — Fig. 21 A.

Leaves spreading or erecto-patent, in exceptional cases slightly secund, when dry twisted, flexuose, from lanceolate base, narrowly lanceolate, gradually narrowed, subulate, margins in the middle slightly recurved or nearly plane; nerve strong, shortly excurrent; cells in the upper part of the leaf quadrate or shortly rectangular, slightly mamillose, in the lower part cells elongate, becoming rectangular beside the nerve. Capsule erect, cylindrical; peristome brown-red, teeth deeply divided; annulus of large cells. Spores green-brown, very finely papillose, 21—24 μ, mature in early summer. — Tufts green or brownish green, darkgreen or blackish at base, up to 5 cm high. On boulders in forest regions.

Scattered localities. **S** *Dls., Vrm., Hjd., Jmt., Ång., ÅsL., LL.* **N.** found in most provinces. **F.** *Al., Ab., Nyl., Tb., Ks.* (Known only from Fennoscandia).

The largest and prettiest of our *Cynodontium* species. In habit it may resemble *Kiaeria blyttii*. This species is, however, easily recognized by its male inflorescence, see fig. 25 D. *Cynodontium suecicum* as well as all *Cynodontium* species have a more or less recurved leaf margin, while *Kiaeria* has a plane one.

2.   **C. bruntonii** (Sm.) Br. Eur., 1846; (*Dicranum Bruntonii* Sm., Engl. Bot., 1812; *Oncophorus Bruntonii* Lindb., Musci Scand., 1879). — Fig. 21 B.

Leaves narrowly lanceolate, the apical leaves longer and more crowded than the lower; cells in upper part mamillose, small, rounded-quadrate, below the middle becoming gradually rectangular, towards the base enlarged, shortly rectangular. Capsule oval, erect, or nearly so, smooth, contracted at the mouth; annulus not differentiated; peristome yellow or reddish yellow, slightly developed, smooth or with irregular transverse or vertical striation. Spores about 17 μ, brown, finely papillose, mature in early summer. — Dense tufts in clefts of rocks.

Scattered in the western provinces, elsewhere rare. **S.** *Sk., Bl., Sm., Hl., Boh., Vg., Ög., Dsl., Vrm., Nrk.* **N.** *ÖFld. —STrd.* **F.** *Al., Ka.* **D.** *Brnh.* (Europe, Canada ?).

When fruiting easily recognized by the smooth, oval capsule, with slightly developed peristome teeth; when barren it is difficult to separate from the other species of this genus, but the long and somewhat crowded apical leaves are characteristic of the species.

3.   **C. strumiferum** (Hedw.) DNot., Epil., 1869; (*Fissidens strumifer* Hedw., Sp. Musc., 1801; *Oncophorus strumifer* Brid., Br. Univ., 1826; *C. polycarpum* var. *strumiferum* Mönkem., Erg. Bd., 1927). — Fig. 21 C.

Leaves narrowly lanceolate; cells above for the most part highly mamillose, quadrate, 11—12 μ, towards the base rectangular, angular cells slightly enlarged. Capsule curved, with struma; annulus of large cells. Spores about

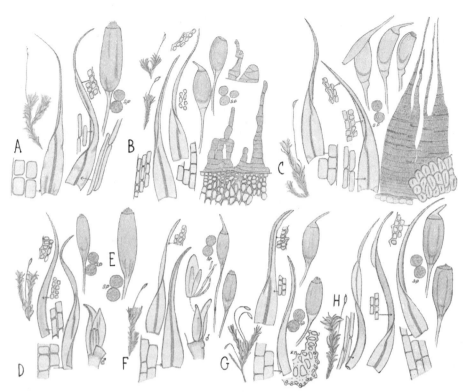

Fig. 21 A *Cynodontium suecicum*, B *C. bruntonii*, C *C. strumiferum*, D *C. polycarpum*, E *C. jenneri*, F *C. tenellum*, G *C. gracilescens*, H *C. fallax*.

20 μ, brown, finely papillose, mature in summer. — Loose tufts, up to 5 cm high, on shaded rocks in the forest reg., but also occasionally found high up in the alpine reg.

Scattered in the eastern provinces, more rare in the western. **S., N., F.** throughout the territory. **D.** *Brnh.* (Europe, Asia, North America).

4. **C. jenneri** (Schimp.) Stirt. in Ann. Scot. Nat. Hist. (*Didymodon Jenneri* Schimp., Howie in Trans. Edinb. Bot. Soc., 1868; *C. polycarpum* var. *laxirete* Dix., Handb. Brit. Moss., 1896; *C. polycarpum* var. *laevifolium* Hag. in Tromsö Mus. Aarsh., 1899; *C. laxirete* Grebe in Hedwigia, 1901; *Oncophorus Jenneri* Williams, N. Am. Fl., 1913). — Fig. 21 E.

Leaf longly lanceolate, margin slightly recurved, towards apex plane; cells in the upper part of the leaf nearly smooth, regular, about 14 μ, rarely up to 20 μ. Capsule large, mostly erect; annulus of 2 rows large, separating cells. Spores about 24 μ, mature in early summer. — Lax tufts on shady rocks.

Scattered in the western provinces, elsewhere rare. **S.** *Bl., Hl., Boh., Dsl., Ög?, Upl.* **N.** *ÖFld.—Trs.* **F.** *Al.* **D.** *Jl., Brnh.* (The western and north-western parts of Europe, North America).

Like the following species but is generally more robust. The leaves are longer, the upper lamina cells are larger, more regularly quadrate and more transparent because less mamillose. The margins of the leaf are nearly plane.

5.   **C. polycarpum** (Hedw.) Schimp., Br. Eur. Coroll., 1855; (*Fissidens poly-carpus* Hedw., Sp. Musc., 1801; *Oncophorus polycarpus* Brid., Br. Univ., 1826). — Fig. 21 D.

Leaves narrowly lanceolate; cells in upper part mamillose, rounded-quadrate, slightly incrassate, below gradually longer, rectangular, towards the base enlarged. Capsule erect or nearly so, oblong-cylindrical, with short neck without struma; annulus of large, separating cells. Spores about 20 µ, brown, finely papillose, mature in summer. — Loose or rather dense tufts, short to several cm high on shaded rocks in the forest region, in mountains only at lower levels.

Widespread, but most common in the western and central provinces. **S., N.** over the greater part of the territorry. **F.** *Al., Ab., Nyl., Ka., St., Tb., Om.* **D.** *Jl.* (Europe, Asia, North America).

There are forms of this species which are difficult to distinguish from the following species. Typical *C. polycarpum* however has acute perigonial leaves, — fig. 21. D, ♂, — *C. tenellum* has obtuse ones, — fig. 21. F, ♂. — The former has an annulus of large separating cells, the latter has the annulus narrow and persistent.

6.   **C. tenellum** (Br. Eur.) Limpr., Krypt.—Fl. Schles., 1877; (*Dicranum gracilescens* γ *tenellum* Br. Eur., 1846, *Oncophorus tenellus* Williams, N. Am. Fl., 1913). — Fig. 21 F.

Leaves narrowly lanceolate, usually less mamillose above than *C. poly-carpum*; perigonial leaves obtuse. Capsules mostly numerous and crowded, erect, comparatively small; annulus narrow and persistent. Spores 15—20 µ, finely papillose, mature in summer. — Dense tufts, 1—3 cm high, on rocks in forest regions.

Frequent in the northern and central parts, rare in the South. **S., N., F.** in most provinces. (Europe, Asia, North America).

7.   **C. gracilescens** (Web. et Mohr) Schimp., Br. Eur. Coroll., 1855; (*Dicra-num gracilescens* Web. et Mohr, Bot. Taschenb., 1807; *Oncophorus gracilescens* Lindb., Musc. Scand., 1879). — Fig. 21 G.

Leaves narrowly lanceolate, usually obtuse, lamina in the upper part of the leaf highly and coarsely mamillose; cells about 7—8 µ, opaque, below the middle gradually rectangular, towards the base enlarged, pellucid, rectangular to quadrate. Seta curved, cygneous when moist. Spores about 20 µ, papillose, mature in summer. — Up to 5 cm high, compact or loose tufts on dry or slightly damp slate rocks or ledges from the alpine region to the upper part of the forest region.

Rare alpine plant. **S.** *TL.?* **N.** *Hord., SoFj., Opl., Hdm., STrd.* (North, West and Central Europe, North America).

Easily recognized by its seta which is cygneous when moist. If sterile, it is distinguishable from the other species of this genus by the rounded leaf-apex and the highly mamillose upper lamina.

8.   **C. fallax** Limpr., Laubm., 1886; (*Dicranum alpestre* β *majus* Wg., Fl. Lapp., 1812). — Fig. 21 H.

Leaves long and narrowly lanceolate; cells in the upper part of the leaf highly and pointedly mamillose, quadrate, 10—13 μ, below smooth, rectangular, elongate beside the nerve, at basal angles enlarged. Capsule erect, annulus narrow, persistent. Spores about 21 μ, brown, papillose, mature in summer. — Loose tufts, up to 5 cm high, on shady, damp rocks.

Rare. **S.** *Sm., Ög., Vg., Dsl., Srm.* **N.** *Tel., Hord., SoFj., Möre, Opl., Nrdl.* (Central Europe, Siberia, Altai).

Robust species with long, narrow, often twisted leaves, with large mamillae.

23. Oncophorus Brid., Br. Univ., 1826.

Autoicous. Androecium bud-like, with 3—6 perigonial bracts. Stem leaves from a clasping or subclasping base, narrowly lanceolate, spreading or flexuose when moist, crisped when dry; nerve strong, excurrent or percurrent, in cross section with 2 stereid bands; cells above quadrate or rounded-quadrate, smooth or nearly so, below rectangular, angular cells ± enlarged. Capsule curved, asymmetrical, without striae but furrowed when empty and dry; struma distinct; annulus not differentiated; peristome reddish, teeth divided towards the middle, below point-striated, above papillose and yellowish. Stem with large central strand.

I Leaf margin recurved in the middle; angular cells enlarged . . . . 1. *O. virens*
II Leaf margin flat; angular cells only slightly differentiated . . . . 2. *O. wahlenbergii*

1. O. virens (Hedw.) Brid., Br. Univ., 1826; (*Dicranum virens* Hedw., Sp. Musc., 1801; *Cynodontium virens* Schimp., Br. Eur. Coroll., 1855). — Fig. 22 A.
Leaves from broad, subclasping base gradually narrowed, lanceolate, acute; margin entire or irregularly serrate above; angular cells pellucid, enlarged, 2—3-stratose. Capsule oblong, curved, pale brown. Spores 22—28 μ, green-brown, finely papillose, mature in early summer. — Tufts soft, green or yellowish green, 1—5 cm high, more or less radiculose. On damp soil, of banks and shores, wet rocks and rotten tree stumps.

Common in the mountains, rare in the lowlands. **S., N., F.** in most provinces. (Europe, Morocco, Asia, North America).

Var. **serratus** (Br. Eur.) Schimp., Br. Eur. Coroll., 1855; (*Dicranum serratum* Br. Eur., 1847). — Fig. 22 A, a. — The margin of the upper part of the leaf is coarsely and distinctly serrated. This form is found especially in running water and is perhaps only a modification of the type.

2. O. wahlenbergii Brid., Br. Univ., 1826; (*Cynodontium Wahlenbergii* Hartm., Scand. Fl., 1871). — Fig. 22 B.
Leaves from broad, oval sheathing base rapidly narrowed to a long, flexuose point; margin flat, entire or the upper part sometimes serrated; cells at basal angles thin-walled, not or only slightly enlarged, other leaf-cells especially in older leaves rounded-quadrate, incrassate. Capsule brown, shortly oval, curved. Spores 20—25 μ, green-brown, finely papillose, mature in early summer. — Soft, light or dark green tufts in similar localities as the preceding species.

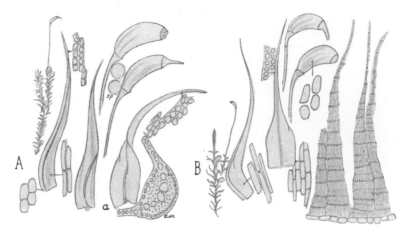

Fig. 22 *Oncophorus virens*, a forma *serratus*, B *O. wahlenbergii*.

Common in the mountains, rare in the lowlands. **S., N., F.** in most provinces. (Europe, North and Central Asia, North America).

A variable species regarding the height and density of the tufts, etc. — Forma **compactus** (Funck.) Br. Eur. grows on dry soil. The tufts are dense and compact; — forma **elongatus** (Hag.) C. Jens., on the other hand, is a large, luxuriant, light-green, loose-tufted form on damp, shady soil; — var. **alpestris** H. Perss. is a mountain form, with distinctly serrated leaves and very small, nearly erect capsules, often without a struma; — var. **gracilis** (Broth.) Arn. et Jens. is a tall form, with short, entire, distant leaves. Occurs on damp soil of banks etc.

24. **Dicranoweisia** Lindb. in Öfv. K. V. A. Förh., 1864.

Autoicous. Androecium bud-like, below the perichaetium. Leaves entire from lanceolate base, gradually narrowed to a long subula, spreading when moist; nerve ending in the apex, in cross section with two stereid bands; cells in the upper part of the leaf shortly rectangular or quadrate, smooth or slightly papillose, towards the base elongate. Capsule erect, smooth, symmetrical; peristome teeth entire or split at the apex, papillose or ± smooth. Stem with central strand.

I   Leaf margins narrowly recurved; lamina smooth; angular
    cells not differentiated . . . . .1. *D. cirrata*
II Leaf margins flat; lamina finely striate; angular cells
    differentiated . . . . .2. *D. crispula*

1.   D. cirrata (Hedw.) Lindb. in Öfv. K. V. A. Förh., 1864; (*Weisia cirrata* Hedw., Sp. Musc., 1801). — Fig. 23 A.

Leaves spreading, crisped when dry; margins recurved in the middle; cells in upper part of the leaf shortly rectangular to quadrate, in margin bistratose, towards the base cells enlarged, thin-walled, rectangular, homogeneous. Capsule cylindrical; annulus 1 row of large, easily separating cells; peristome red-brown, ± smooth below, above pale and papillose. Spores brown-green, 15—18 μ, slightly papillose, mature in autumn and winter. — Soft cushions on tree stumps, tree roots or rocks, etc., in the lowlands

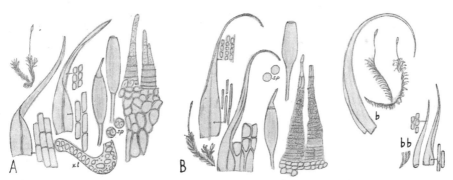

Fig. 23 A *Dicranoweisia cirrata,* B *D. crispula,* b forma *secunda,* bb var. *compacta.*

Widespread in the southern provinces. **S.** *Sk.* — *Vrm., Upl., Öl., Gtl.* **N.** *ÖFld., Akh., Busk., VFld., VAgd., Rog.* **F.** *Al.* **D.** throughout the country. (Europe, Canaries, Madeira, North Africa, Asia, North America, Hawaii).

Like *Orthodicranum montanum* but this has a serrate leaf apex and distinctly angular cells.

2. D. crispula (Hedw.) Lindb. in Öfv. K. V. A. Förh., 1864; (*Weissia crispula* Hedw., Sp. Musc., 1801). — Fig. 23 B.

Leaves spreading, flexuose, above sometimes secund, crisped when dry, margins flat; cells in the upper part rounded, shortly rectangular to quadrate, striate, — towards the base cells elongate, incrassate, — angular cells differentiated, finally brown. Capsule cylindrical; annulus absent; peristome reddish brown, teeth coarsely papillose above, irregularly point-striated below. Spores yellow-green, 10—15 μ, very finely papillose, mature in spring or early summer. — Soft, yellowish to dark-green cushions or mats on rocks and soil of siliceous or calcareous origin.

Very common in mountains, elsewhere rare. **S., N., F.** in most provinces but absent from the extreme South. (Europe, Asia, North America, Greenland).

Forma **secunda** Arn. et Jens. — Fig. 23 B, b. — More robust than the type. Leaves secund. On ground flushed with water from melting snow. — Var. **compacta** (Schleich.) Lindb. (*Grimmia compacta* Schleich., *D. compacta* Schimp. — Fig. 23 B, bb. — Leaves small, short-pointed; cells somewhat smaller than those of the type; in the lower part of the leaf cells shortly rectangular. Small, compact, dark tufts on soil or rocks in reg. alp.

This very variable species is always easily recognized by the usually numerous, smooth, erect capsules. Under the microscope the lamina appears striate.

25. Arctoa (Br. Eur., 1846, emend.),
Hag. in K. N. V. Selsk. Skr., 1914.

Autoicous. Androecium bud-like, below the gynoecium. Leaves lanceolate, more or less channelled; nerve excurrent, in cross section with homogeneous cells; in the upper part of the leaf cells rounded quadrate or rectangular, irregular and incrassate, becoming longer towards the base, — angular cells

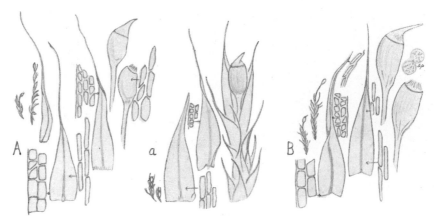

Fig. 24 A *Arctoa fulvella*, a var. *anderssonii*, B *A. hyperborea*.

somewhat enlarged, quadrate or shortly rectangular. Seta yellow, thick;
capsule erect, broadly oval, symmetrical or slightly asymmetrical, furrowed
when dry and empty; peristome brown-red, papillose above, vertically point-
striated below, teeth split or perforated to the middle. — Arctic-alpine or
high-alpine species growing on soil or rocks.

I Nerve very longly excurrent; peristome teeth spreading
   when dry . . . . .1. *A. fulvella*
II Nerve shortly excurrent; peristome teeth not spreading. . . . .2. *A. hyperborea*

1. A. fulvella (Dicks.) Br. Eur., 1846; *Bryum fulvellum* Dicks., Fl. Crypt.
    Brit., 1801; Dicranum fulvellum Sm., Fl. Brit., 1804). — Fig. 24 A.
   Leaves erecto-patent or somewhat secund, from lanceolate base narrowed
to a long, rough, slender subula; nerve very longly excurrent; cells incrassate,
above irregularly rounded-rectangular, towards the margins rounded-quadrate
or triangular, below towards nerve cells elongate, — angular cells enlarged,
shortly rectangular, forming an oblong group. Capsule symmetrical or slightly
curved; annulus of 2 rows of cells; peristome teeth red, lanceolate-subulate,
cleft to the middle or perforated, widely spreading when dry; lid obliquely
rostellate. Spores about 20 μ, finely papillose, mature in summer. — Dense,
slightly glossy tufts, 1—4 cm high on siliceous soil and rocks (rarely on calciferous substrata) in high-alpine regions, also in snow-bed communities with
Cesia-species; is seldom seen below the willow region.

   Scattered, on exposed ridges and mountain summits. **S.** *Hjd—TL.* **N.** *Busk.—*
—Fnm. **F.** *Lk., Le., Li.* (North, West, and Central Europe, Asia, North America).

   Var. **anderssonii** (Wich.) H. Perss. et Uggla in Sv. Bot. Tidskr., 1942 (*A.
Anderssonii* Wich. in Flora, 1859, *Dicranum Anderssonii* Schimp., Syn. Musc.
Eur., 1860). — Fig. 24 A, a. — Leaves with shorter subula; cells in the upper
part of the leaf mostly irregularly quadrate; nerve more shortly excurrent. Perichaetial leaves large, with sheathing base, reaching above the capsule. Seta very
short; capsule usually erect and symmetrical. Spores about 27 μ, brown, finely
papillose, mature in summer. — On rocks. — **S.** *LL., TL.* (North Europe, arct.
North America, Greenland).

2. A. hyperborea (Sm.) Br. Eur., 1846; (*Dicranum hyperboreum* Sm., Fl. Brit., 1804; *Cynodontium hyperboreum* Hag. in K. N. V. Selsk. Skr., 1914). — Fig. 24 B.

Leaves erecto-patent, from oval, lanceolate base, narrowed to a long subula; nerve excurrent; cells incrassate, in the upper part of the leaf irregularly rounded-quadrate or shortly rectangular, elongate below towards nerve, — angular cells slightly enlarged, quadrate or shortly rectangular. Seta short; capsule symmetrical or slightly asymmetrical; annulus developed, separating; peristome large, teeth divided or perforated approximately to the middle. Spores up to 30 μ, brown, finely papillose, mature in summer. — Tufts dark green, dense, 1—5 cm high on dry or slightly damp siliceous rocks or in rock crevices.

Rare arctic-alpine plant. **S.** *Jmt.—TL.* **N.** *ÖAgd.—Nrdl., Trs.* **F.** *Le.* (Jan Mayen, North America, Greenland).

26. Kiaeria Hag. in K. N. V. Selsk. Skr., 1914.

Autoicous, polyoicous. Androecium bud-like. Leaves lanceolate, with a long, finely channelled, serrulate subula; nerve excurrent, in cross section with homogeneous cells (*K. glacialis* usually with few stereids); cells in the upper part of the leaf short or long, ± papillose, towards the base cells elongate with or without pores, angular cells differentiated, sometimes inflated and brown. Seta long; capsule erect or curved, symmetrical or asymmetrical, with a more or less distinct struma; exothecial cells irregular, somewhat incrassate; annulus of large, separating cells or of small, persistent cells; peristome brown-red, teeth divided or perforated approximately to the middle, above papillose, yellowish, vertically point-striated below; lid usually rostellate. Spores 14—20 μ, brown, finely papillose, mature in summer. Loosely tufted and with sparse radicles. Arctic, alpine or subalpine plants.

I Cells in the upper part of the leaf elongate, smooth, angular cells distinct
   1 Large species; cells in the whole leaf more or less porose;
      annulus of one row of large cells ....1. *K. glacialis*
   2 Slender; lamina cells porose only in the lower part of
      the leaf; annulus of 2—3 rows of cells ....2. *K. starkei*
II Cells in the upper part of the leaf rectangular or quadrate,
   slightly papillose, angular cells less distinct
   1 Leaves regularly falcato-secund; annulus of small
      persistent cells ....3. *K. falcata*
   2 Leaves flexuose, somewhat crisped when dry; annulus of
      3 rows of cells, separating ....4. *K. blyttii*

1. K. glacialis (Berggr.) Hag. in K. N. V. Selsk. Skr., 1914; (*Dicranum Starkei* var. *molle* Wils., Br. Brit., 1855; *Dicranum glaciale* Berggr. in Act. Univ. Lund., 1865; *Dicranum arcticum* Schimp., Br. Eur., suppl., 1866). Fig. 25 A.

Autoicous. Androecium close below the perichaetium. Leaves erecto-patent or secund; cells in the greatest part of the leaf elongate, more or less porose, angular cells very distinct, inflated, dark-brown. Capsule curved, slightly strumose, furrowed when dry; annulus of one row of large cells, separating; exothecial cells elongate, somewhat incrassate. — Large, loose tufts on soil,

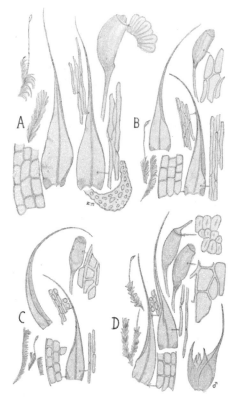

Fig. 25 A *Kiaeria molle*, B *K. starkei*,
C *K. falcata*, D *K. blyttii*.

on earth-covered rocks, in snow-beds etc., from the alpine region to the upper part of the wood limit, rarely lower.

Scattered, sometimes frequent. **S. N. F.** in mountain regions. (North Europe, Faeroes, Scotland, Kamtchatka, Alaska, Labrador, Greenland).

2.   **K. starkei** (Web. et Mohr) Hag. in K. N. V. Selsk. Skr., 1911; (*Dicranum Starkei* Web. et Mohr, Bot. Taschenb., 1807). Fig. 25 B.

Autoicous. Androecium close below the perichaetium. Leaves falcate, sometimes flexuose or erecto-patent; cells in the upper part of the leaf mostly elongate, rectangular, towards the base more or less porose, — angular cells well differentiated, brown, sometimes inflated. Capsule slightly curved, thin-walled, ± furrowed and strumose when dry and empty, annulus of 2—3 rows of cells, separating. — In loose tufts on similar substrata and in similar localities as the preceding species.

Frequent. **S. N. F.** in mountain regions. (Europe, Asia, North America, the east part of Greenland).

Forma **glacialis** (Zett.) C. Jens. is a form found in snow-beds in reg. alp. The leaves may be nearly erect, the tufts dark-green, low and compact.

For the difference of the present species from *K. falcata* and *K. blyttii*, see under the latter species.

3.   **K. falcata** (Hedw.) Hag. in K. N. V. Selsk. Skr., 1914; (*Dicranum falcatum* Hedw., Sp. Musc., 1801). — Fig. 25 C.

Autoicous. Androecium just below the perichaetium. Leaves regularly falcato-secund; cells in the upper part of the leaf rectangular, occasionally quadrate, — towards the base cells narrowly elongate, smooth, incrassate, — angular cells brownish, moderately differentiated. Capsule erect or slightly curved, more or less strumose, — exothecial cells incrassate, irregular, 5—6 rows of small, rounded, irregular cells at mouth; annulus of small, persistent cells. — Compact, low, green or yellowish green, somewhat glossy mats in damp or wet places, in snow-beds, etc., in alpine regions, chiefly on siliceous substrata.

Not rare in higher mountains. **S.** *Hjd.—TL.* **N.** *Busk.—Fnm.* **F.** *Le.* (North, West and Central Europe, Asia, North America).

Falcate forms of *K. starkei* may be confused with *K. falcata*, but the lamina cells of this species are shorter than those of *K. starkei*. The cells towards the base make an impression of regularity, the cell-walls being uniformly thickened, without pores. *K. starkei* has in the lower part of the leaf more or less porose cells.

4. **K. blyttii** (Schimp.) Broth., Laubm. Fennosk., 1923; (*Dicranum Blyttii* Schimp., Br. Eur.; 1847, *Dicranum Schisti* Lindb. in Act. Soc. Sc. Fenn., 1871). Fig. 25 D.

Polyoicous. Androecium far below the perichaetium or terminal on a short branch, occasionally terminal on separate ♂ plants. Leaves erecto-patent or flexuose, slightly crisped when dry; cells above rectangular to quadrate, towards the base (especially beside the nerve) elongate and ± porose, angular cells mostly well developed. Capsule slightly curved, indistinctly strumose; annulus large, of three rows of cells. — Soft, dark-green tufts on rocks from the lowlands to high in the mountains.

Scattered in the South, widespread in the North. **S. N. F.** in most provinces. (North, West and Central Europe, North America).

This species is sometimes difficult to recognize. The cells of the leaf vary; the shorter cells in the upper part of the leaf sometimes continue down the margin towards the base. However, there are also forms with elongated cells in the upper part of the lamina. These may be like flexuose forms of *K. starkei*. The position of the male flower of *K. blyttii* is a very good distinguishing character. *K. blyttii* has leaves slightly papillose above, *K starkei* smooth. — The sterile, small, dark forms of *K. starkei* with erect-spreading or flexuose leaves, which are found in snow-beds at high altitudes, can be very difficult to determine. However, I have never seen *K. blyttii* in snow-beds, while *K. starkei* is frequent in such habitats.

K. blyttii may also be confused with *Cynodontium suecicum*; for distinguishing characters see under the latter species.

27. **Dicranum** Hedw., Sp. Musc., 1801.

Dioicous. Androecium bud-like. ♂ plants minute, in the radicles of normal plants, or larger and forming separate tufts or mingled with the ♀ plants. Leaves for the most part narrowly lanceolate, falcato-secund, flexuose or erecto-patent; nerve wide or narrow, excurrent or ending below the apex, in cross section with 2 stereid bands (expt. *D. fragilifolium*, which has no stereids); cells smooth or mamillose on the dorsal side towards the apex, in the upper part of the leaf cells long or short, with or without pores, elongate and more or less porose below, angular cells well developed, inflated, coloured, usually bi- or multistratose, between the angular cells and the nerve often bistratose subcortical cells. Seta long; capsule curved and asymmetrical, rarely erect and symmetrical, stomata 1—2 rows at the base of the capsule, annulus differentiated or absent; peristome-teeth divided into 2 (4) approximately to the middle, striated, very seldom smooth, usually vertically point-striated below, papillose above. Lid long, rostrate. Calyptra cucullate, entire at the base, usually falling with the lid. Spores papillose, mature in summer. Stem with central strand. This genus is most frequent in the northern coniferous forest and mountains and in the arctic; in tropical and subtropical regions, it is represented only in the mountains, while in the Southern hemisphere it is replaced by the almost exclusively Southern-Hemisphere genus *Dicranoloma*.

I Mainly elongate, porose, prosenchymatous cells also in the
  upper part of the leaf; capsule without annulus of large cells
  1 Leaves distinctly transversely undulate, in the upper
    part of the leaf spinosely serrate from above to the
    middle ....1. *D. rugosum*
  2 Leaves not or only slightly transversely undulate
    a The apex of the leaf broad and short; nerve thin and
      narrow; lamina in the upper part rugose or undulate.......2. *D. bonjeani*
    aa Leaves acute or subulate, nerve strong
    b Nerve with 4 usually serrate lamellae at back above .....3. *D. scoparium*
    bb Nerve furrowed and usually serrate at back above.........4. *D. majus*
II Mainly quadrate or rectangular, parenchymatous cells in
  the upper part of the leaves; capsule with annulus of large
  separating cells
  1 Capsule more or less curved; peristome teeth vertically
    point-striated below, papillose above; (in Scandinavia
    most common in the coniferous forest and mountain
    regions)
    a Leaves in the upper part rugose or transversely-
      undulate
    b Lamina and nerve at back in the upper part of the
      leaf rough with mamillose spinelike or conical project-
      ing cells; leaf base ovate
    c Cells in the upper part of the leaf irregularly qua-
      drate, walls not sinuose; leaf with a long, gradually
      narrowed, falcate apex...............................5. *D. robustum*
    cc Cells in the upper part of the leaf very irregular,
      triangular, quadrate, with sinuose walls; leaves
      from broadly ovate base rapidly narrowed to a
      lanceolate subula ....6. *D. spurium*
    bb Lamina and nerve smooth or with low mamillae
      above at back; leaf base lanceolate ....7. *D. bergeri*
    aa Lamina not rugose or transversely undulate
    b Leaves not fragile; nerve in cross section with
      stereids
    c Transverse sections of the upper part of the leaf
      like a pair of tongs, with large projections between
      the cells, — fig. 27 D, xl and xn. ....8. *D. muehlenbeckii*
    cc The cross sections from the upper part of the leaf
      with a rounded appearance and with smaller pro-
      jections between the cells, — fig. 28 xl and xn
    d Leaf-cells a little thickened; loosely or densely
      tufted ....9. *D. fuscescens*
    dd Leaf-cells very incrassate; tufts usually firm,
      compact, tomentose ....10. *D. elongatum*
    bb Leaves fragile; nerve in cross section without
      stereids ....11. *D. fragilifolium*
  2 Capsule erect or nearly so; peristome teeth smooth or
    slightly striated; (in Scandinavia in the western or
    southern provinces, on rocks or on stones in deciduous
    woods)
    a Lamina unistratose, but sometimes bistratose at the
      margin near the apex ....12. *D. scottianum*
    aa Lamina bistratose in the upper part of the leaf beside
      the nerve..13. *D. fulvum*

Sect. I. Dicrana scoparia: ♂ plants minute, rarely large in separate
tufts. The upper part of the leaf channelled or sometimes tubular, serrated
at margin; nerve wide or narrow, the dorsal side of the upper part with la-

mellae or furrowed; cells above usually elongate, porose, most angular cells rectangular. Capsule without separate annulus cells, peristome teeth below point-striated, above papillose.

1. D. rugosum Brid., Sp. Musc. 1806; (*D. undulatum* Sturm, Deutschl. Fl., 1812; *D. undulatum* Br. eur., 1847) — Fig. 26 A.

Leaves elongate-lanceolate, spreading, rarely slightly secund, distinctly transversely undulate; the margins spinosely serrate in the upper part; nerve narrow, ending below the apex, with 2 (— 4) sharply serrated lamellae at back above, — Fig. 26 A, xn. — Seta yellow, 1 — 5 from the same perichaetium. — A tall and robust species in wide, loose, soft, yellowish green mats; stems with dense, albescent tomentum. Grows on shaded, damp soil, especially in coniferous forests.

Very common in the woods of the lowlands, rare in the mountains. **S. N. F. D.** throughout the territory. (Europe, Asia, North America).

A characteristic species. Under unfavourable conditions, however, there are more or less reduced forms of this as well as of the other species of *Dicrana scoparia*. Forms with more or less entire leaves and with lamellae at the back of the nerve less developed may be difficult to determine. Leaf shape and the usually transversely undulate upper lamina with wide cells, the coarsely serrated margins and the two well-developed middle lamellae of the nerve serve to distinguish this species from the other species of the section. — Luxuriant forms are as a rule easily identified.

2. D. bonjeani DNot. in Lisa Elencho, 1837; (*D. undulatum* Turn., Musc. Hib., 1804; *D. palustre* Br. Eur., 1847). — Fig. 26 B.

Leaves lanceolate, narrowly acuminate, with a broad, often obtuse point; lamina for the most part slightly transversely undulate; nerve thin and narrow, ending below the apex, in the upper part with 2(—4) low, smooth or serrated lamellae at the back. Seta yellowish or reddish green, solitary or two together. — Soft green or yellowish green, rarely dark or brown-green tufts on damp soil or rocks, etc., from the lowlands to the mountains but rarely above the wood regions.

Not uncommon. **S. N. F. D.** throughout the territory. (Europe, Azores, Asia, North America.

This species is most closely allied to *D. undulatum*. It is, however, distinguished from that by a narrower nerve with much lower lamellae; the cells in the upper part of the leaf are smaller and the margins are more lowly and obtusely serrate. — Forms with falcate leaves may be very like *D. scoparium*, but in cross sections of the nerve *D. bonjeani* has fewer guide cells than this species and only 2 less developed lamellae at the back of the nerve.

3. D. scoparium Hedw., Sp. Musc., 1801. — Fig. 26 C.

Leaves lanceolate, more or less longly subulate, erecto-patent or falcato-secund; lamina usually straight, seldom transversely rugose; nerve in the upper part with 4 dorsal serrated lamellae. Seta yellowish or brownish red, solitary. — Usually large, robust, green or brownish green tufts or mats on various substrata, on dry or damp soil, on shaded or exposed rocks. However, it reaches its highest development in coniferous forest.

DICRANACEAE

Tab. 26 A *Dicranum rugosum*, B *D. bonjeani*, C *D. scoparium*, D *D. majus*.

Very common. **S. N. F. D.** throughout the territory. (Europe, Azores, Madeira, Canaries, Asia, North America, New Zealand).

Its habit is very variable; there are forms with entire or nearly entire leaves and with the lamellae of the nerve more or less reduced, there are also luxuriant forms with sharply serrated leaves or with lamina ± rugose. — For the difference between this species and *D. undulatum* and *D. bonjeani* see note under the respective species. — A reliable character for distinction between a doubtful *D. scoparium* and a doubtful *D. majus* seems to be afforded by the cells of the lamina. In cross section the lamina-cells of *D. majus* are rectangular (Fig. 26 D, xn) while those of *D. scoparium* are quadrate (Fig. 26 C, xn).

4. D. majus Turn., Musc. Hib., 1804. — Fig. 26 D.

Leaves lanceolate with a long, usually falcato-secund subula, leaves rarely shorter and erect or erecto-patent; margins in the upper part of the leaves more or less sharply, irregularly serrulate; nerve at back in the upper part of the leaf furrowed and serrate, in cross section of the nerve a continuous layer of dorsal cells, some of them projecting outwards towards the apex of the leaf (fig. 26 D xn). Seta yellow or brown, 1—5 from the same perichaetium. — A large and robust species, in soft tufts or mats on shaded soil in woods but it also occurs high in the alpine regions.

Common. **S. N. F. D.** throughout the territory. (Europe, Asia, North America).

As with the last species, *D. majus* is also very variable, perhaps the most variable of all. Especially in the mountains there are a great number of forms. High in the alpine region are forms with short, ± erect, nearly smooth leaves, the cells in the upper part sometimes short, nearly quadrate. Also in bogs on lower levels similar or other variations occur. Whether all these forms are only modifications of the type or whether there are genetical differences between them will be shown by future research.

For the difference between this and the preceding species, see note under the latter.

Sect. II. Dicrana spuria: ♂ plant minute, in the radicles of the ♀ plants. Leaves in the upper part channelled, in cross section like a pair of tongs — fig. 27 D, xl, — when dry apex curled or twisted; margin serrate, nerve mostly strong, rough, with mamillose cells at back in the upper part; cells in the upper lamina short, irregular or quadrate, usually without pores, below cells elongate with or without pores, angular cells quadrate or shortly rectangular, numerous. Capsule with annulus of 1(—2) rows of large cells; peristome below point-striated, above papillose.

5. D. robustum Blytt in Br. Eur., 1847; (*D. elatum* Lindb. in Hedwigia, 1868). — Fig. 27 A.

Leaves from ovate base, longly subulate, secund or falcato-secund; margins serrated towards the apex; nerve excurrent, rough at back of apex; lamina rugose, rough with high mamillae at back in the upper part, cells elongate and porose below, shorter to irregularly quadrate with straight walls above. — Tufts soft, robust, usually 10—15 cm high on soil or damp rocks in coniferous forest.

Not uncommon. **S.** *Sm.—TL., Gtl.* **N.** *ÖFld.—Trs.* **F.** throughout the country. (North Europe, Yenisei, Sakhalin).

6. D. spurium Hedw., Sp. Musc., 1801. — Fig. 27 B.

Leaves erecto-patent, from an ovate base quickly contracted to an acute, serrate, transversely undulate apex, when dry the upper part of the leaf is incurved and curled; nerve ending below the apex, rough upwards at back; cells elongate and porose below, above irregular, triangular or quadrate, with sinuose walls, at back of leaf cells highly mamillose. — In lax or dense tufts, 2—6 cm high, on moors, dry soils, rocks, etc., in the coniferous forest.

Not uncommon. **S.** *Sk.—LyL., Öl., Gtl.* **N.** *ÖFld.—Fnm.* **F.** throughout the country. **D.** *Jl., Fy., Sj., Brnh.* (Europe, Asia, North America).

Forma **pseudo-elatum** Tolf, a large and luxuriant form, like *D. robustum*. *D. spurium* has the top leaves erect, those of *D. robustum* are secund.

7. D. bergeri Bland., Musci Frond. Exc., 1804; (*D. undulatum* Brid., Sp. Musc., 1806; *D. intermedium* Crome, Samml. II, 1805; *D. Schraderi* Web. et Mohr, Bot. Taschenb., 1807). — Fig. 27 C.

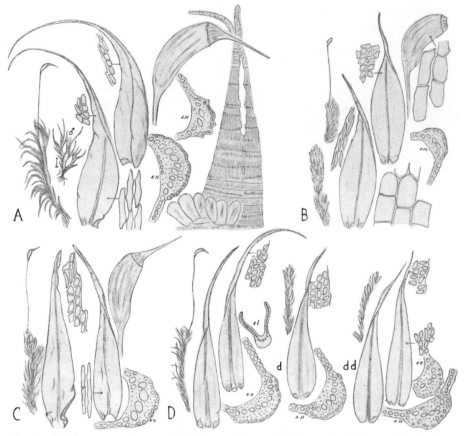

Fig. 27 A *Dicranum robustum*, B *D. spurium*, C *D. bergeri*, D *D. muehlenbeckii*,
d var. *brevifolium*, dd var. *acutifolium*.

Leaves erecto-patent or slightly secund, transversely undulate, from lanceolate base gradually narrowed to a broad, more or less obtuse apex; nerve
ending just below the apex; cells elongate and porose below, at apex quadrate
to shortly rectangular, slightly irregular. — In large, dense, tomentose tufts
on damp or wet substrata, in meadows and bogs in the lowlands as well as in
the mountains.

More or less common. **S. N. F.** throughout the territory. **D.** *Jl.*, *Sj.*, *Flst.* (Europe,
Asia, North America, Greenland).

A characteristic species in dense, tomentose tufts, mostly in wet places. The
leaves are distinctly transversely undulate, the apex is broad, often obtuse.

8. D. muehlenbeckii Br. Eur., 1847. — Fig. 27 D.

Leaves erecto-patent or slightly secund, from ovate-lanceolate base gradually
narrowed to a long, fine, serrate subula; nerve strong, excurrent; lamina
appears striated due to large projections between the cells; cells below elongate,

with or without pores, angular cells quadrate, numerous, cells in the upper part of the leaf quadrate, rhomboid ± irregular. Seta yellowish red, capsule cylindrical, curved, and striated. — In large, dense, tomentose tufts or carpets on damp or dry soil or rocks, preferably on somewhat calcareous soil.

More or less common. **S. N. F.** throughout the territory. (Europe, Asia, North America).

The Scandinavian forms of this species have generally shorter leaves than the type form, the apex is shorter and broader, the tufts are more loose. This form is named var. **brevifolium** Lindb. in Bot. Not., 1865; (*D. brevifolium* Lindb., Musci Scand., 1879). — Fig. 27 D, d. — I have not found a distinct difference between the type and this var.; I think there is a gradual variation from the type with a long, fine subula to var. *brevifolium* with shorter leaves, and then further to the mountainous or arctic form var. **acutifolium** (Lindb. et Arn.) Nyh. in Bot. Not., 1953. (*D. Bergeri* var. *acutifolium* Lindb. et Arn. in K. V. A. Handl., 1890; *D. acutifolium* C. Jens., Skand. Bladmossfl., 1939). — Fig. 27 D, dd. — The latter has leaves like those of var. *brevifolium,* but the cells in the upper part of the leaf are more irregular and sometimes porose. The tufts are usually robust and ± loose. Occurs in the mountains ascending high up in the alpine region.

Forms of *D. muehlenbeckii* may in habit be like forms of *D. fuscescens,* but the cross section of the leaf which is like a pair of tongs — Fig. 27 D, xl. — in *D. muehlenbeckii* is rounded in *D. fuscescens* — Fig. 28 xl. —. *D. muehlenbeckii* has also, in cross section of the leaf, large projections between the cells; these are small in *D. fuscescens.* The male plants of *D. muehlenbeckii* are minute, 1—2 mm, those of *D. fuscescens* are as large as the ♀ plants.

Sect. III. Dicrana fuscescentia: ♂ plants large in separate tufts or mingled with the ♀ plants. Leaves in the upper part tubular; margins more or less serrate; nerve usually wide, at the back of the apex mostly smooth, sometimes mamillose; cells in the upper part of the leaf quadrate, regular or irregular, usually without pores, below cells elongate, smooth or more or less porose, angular cells rectangular. Capsule curved, with annulus of (1—)3 rows of large cells; peristome below point-striated, above papillose.

9. D. fuscescens Turn., Musc. Hib., 1804. — Fig. 28.

Androecium at the top of the stem, ♂ plants are like the ♀ plants. Leaves erecto-patent, flexuose or secund, from a narrowly lanceolate base, longly subulate; margin above serrate; nerve strong, usually excurrent, in its upper part smooth or rough at back; cells above mostly quadrate, smooth to mamillose at back, below elongate, linear, ± porose. Seta yellowish; capsule curved, asymmetrical, striated, furrowed when dry and empty. — Tufts 1——6(—10) cm high, soft, dull, somewhat tomentose, on rotten tree stumps, soil or rocks from the lowlands to high in the mountains.

Fig. 28 *Dicranum fuscescens,* a var. *congestum*

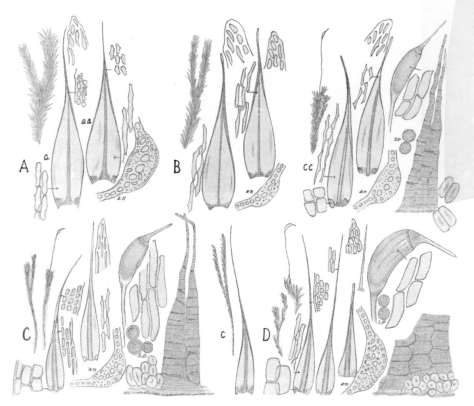

Fig. 29 A *Dicranum spadiceum*, a leaf of a plant from Pyrenees, leg. J. E. Zetterstedt, aa leaf of a plant from TL., B *D. angustum*, C *D. elongatum*, c a plant with longer leaves, cc ssp. *groenlandicum*, D *D. fragilifolium*.

Very common in the northern and central provinces, rare in the South. **S. N. F.** in all provinces, **D.** *Jl.*, *Sj.*, *Brnh.* (Europe, Asia, North America).

A variable species. The tufts can be robust or tender, the leaves long and fine and falcato-secund or short and erect-spreading. Var. **congestum** (Brid.) Husn.; (*D. congestum* Brid.) — fig. 28 a, — is a form with irregular cells in the upper part of the leaf. — The forms with irregular cells are the most common ones of this species in the north of Scandinavia. In the mountains to high up in the alpine regions there are sometimes forms with very irregular, ± porose cells in the upper part of the leaf.

10. D. elongatum Schleich., Pl. Crypt. Helv. Exc., 1805. — Fig. 29 C.

Leaves appressed to erecto-patent, sometimes slightly secund, from a narrow, lanceolate base, longly and finely subulate, entire or slightly dentate at the extreme apex; nerve shortly excurrent or percurrent; cells incrassate, below more or less porose, above smooth, rounded-rectangular or rounded-quadrate. Capsule relatively small, slightly curved; peristome brownish-red, at apex papillose, below closely vertically point-striated. Spores 20—28 μ, closely papillose. — Usually in dense, compact tufts, closely matted with reddish-brown tomentum, occurring on rocks and soil, together with *Sphagna* in peat-mosses, etc.

Very common in the mountains to high in the alpine region, elsewhere rare. **S.** *Vrm.—TL.* **N.** in the mountains. **F.** *Kb., Sb., Ks., Lk., Le., Li., Lps.* (Europe, Asia, North America, Greenland).

A variable species with regard to the density of the tufts and the length of the leaves. However, this species is characterized by the narrow leaves with wide nerve and strongly incrassate, rounded cells in the upper part of the leaf.

Subsp. **groenlandicum** (Brid.) C. Jens., Skand. Bladmossfl., 1939; (*D. groenlandicum* Brid., Mant. Musc., 1819; *D. tenuinerve* Zett. in K. V. A. Handl., 1876). — Fig. 29 C, cc.

Leaves from ovate-lanceolate base, narrowed to a smooth, tubular, obtuse apex; nerve strong, ending below the apex; cells strongly incrassate, porose throughout. Capsule relatively small, slightly curved; peristome orange-coloured, vertically point-striated, with a pale, smooth apex. Spores 20—24 μ, closely papillose. — In large, dense, glossy-green or brownish-green tufts, occurs on damp moors or in peat-mosses, etc., from the upper sub-alpine to high in the alpine region.

Scattered localities. **S.** *TL.* **N.** *ÖFld.—Fnm.* (Europe, Asia, North America, Greenland).

The tufts of subsp. *groenlandicum* are somewhat more robust than the type of *D. elongatum*. The leaves are broader below, the nerve narrower. The best character for distinction, however, is afforded by the elongate, strongly incrassate, and porose cells in the upper part of the leaf. — Compare forms of *D. fuscescens* and *D. muehlenbeckii* with porose cells in the upper part of the leaves.

11. D. fragilifolium Lindb. in Schimp., Syn. Musc. Eur., 1860. — Fig. 29 D.

Leaves erecto-patent or slightly secund, rigid, with a fragile apex, from a lanceolate base, finely subulate; nerve strong, longly excurrent; cells below elongate, porose, at the apex shorter, quadrate to rectangular, smooth. Capsule arcuate, striated. Spores about 24 μ, finely papillose. — Tufts green or yellowish green, dense or rather robust; occurs on decaying tree stumps and logs.

Scattered localities. **S.** *Vrm., Dlr., Mpd.—TL.* **N.** *Akh.—Fnm.* **F.** *Kl., Sb.—Li.* (North Europe, Siberia, arct. North America).

Easily recognized by the very fragile leaf-apex. — In transverse section of the leaf, the cells of the nerve are homogeneous; compare this species with the genus *Kiaeria.*

Sect. IV. Crassidicranum: The upper part of the leaf channelled; margin serrate or entire; nerve strong and broad; cells in the upper part of the leaf quadrate, in cross section with strong projections between the cells, the angular cells for the most part shortly rectangular. Capsule erect, with large annulus-cells; peristome smooth or very slightly striate, or weakly papillose.

12. D. scottianum Turn., Musc. Hib., 1804; (*Campylopus Scottianus* Brid., Mont. Musc., 1819). — Fig. 30 A.

Leaves crowded, rigid, erecto-patent to subsecund, from a lanceolate base gradually narrowed, subulate; nerve strong, excurrent; cells thick-walled,

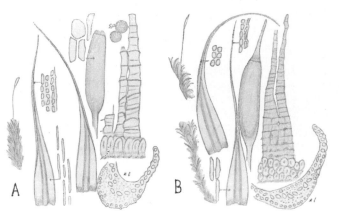

Fig. 30 A *Dicranum scottianum*, B *D. fulvum*.

linear, ± porose below, in the upper part rounded-quadrate or irregular, small; angular cells inflated, partially bistratose, reaching the nerve. Seta thick, yellowish red; capsule erect, cylindrical, yellowish green, smooth. Peristome entire, teeth slightly cleft, apex pale, fragile, smooth or with few, low papillae. — Tufts brown-green, tomentose, robust, occurring on shaded rocks in maritime districts.

Rare. **N.** *ÖFld.—SoFj.* **D.** *Brnh.* (West and Central Europe, Azores, Canaries, Madeira).

13. D. fulvum Hook., Musci Exot., 1820; (*Campylopus fulvus* Kindb., Laubm. Schw. et Norw., 1883). — Fig. 30 B.

Leaves somewhat scattered, erecto-patent or falcato-secund, from an elongate, lanceolate base, gradually narrowed, subulate; margin in the upper part denticulate; nerve broad, indistinct, longly excurrent; cells for the most part regularly quadrate, beside the nerve in the upper half bistratose, (fig. 30 B, xl), in the lower half elongate, porose; angular cells inflated, green to brown, reaching the nerve. Seta thick, yellow or slightly reddish; capsule erect, cylindrical, brownish green to brown, indistinctly striated, more or less furrowed when dry; peristome-teeth cleft to below the middle into 2—3 prongs, at apex pale, yellowish, smooth or slightly papillose, below smooth or slightly striated, prostome visible. — Tufts up to 5 cm high, brownish to dark green, on shaded siliceous rocks in deciduous woods.

Scattered. **S.** *Sk.—Boh.,* *Vg.* **N.** *Tel., Akh.—Hdm.* **D.** *Sj.* (Central Europe, North America).

Var. **viride** (Sull. et Lesq.) Grout, Moss Fl. of N. Am., 1937; (*Campylopus viride* Sull. et Lesq., Musc. Bor. Am., 1856; *D. viride* Lindb. in Hedwigia, 1863). Leaves entire, rigid and fragile, erecto-patent, apical leaves sometimes slightly secund. Tufts more slender than those of the type, green or yellowish green. Occurs on trunks of deciduous trees, seldom on coniferous trees, rocks or soil. Has a more eastern distribution than the type. — **S.** *Sk., Vg.* **N.** *Akh., Hord., Hdm.* **F.** *Ab., Ik., Ta.* (Central Europe, Estonia, Latvia, Caucasus, Yenisei, North America).

Doubtful species.

D. angustum Lindb. in Medd. Soc. F. Fl. Fenn., 1881; (*D. laevidens* Williams, N. Am. Fl., 1913). — Fig. 29 B.

This form is characterized as follows: Leaves erecto-patent to widely spreading, from ovate base narrowed to a tubular, obtuse or somewhat acute, smooth or slightly toothed apex; nerve thin, ending in or below the apex; cells ± thick-walled, porose and elongate to the apex. Capsule with annulus of ± separating cells. Tufts robust, yellowish or brownish green, occurs in wet places, mostly with *Sphagna* in the low-alpine region.

S. N. F. in mountainous districts. (North America).

Future research may show where this form belongs. Perhaps it is a strongly reduced form of *Dicranum majus*.

D. spadiceum Zett. in K. V. A. Handl., 1865. — Fig. 29 A.

Leaves erecto-patent, from an ovate-lanceolate base narrowed to a subulate, tubular apex; margins entire or slightly toothed; nerve excurrent or percurrent, smooth or toothed at the extreme apex; cells in the lower part of the leaf elongate, porose, above shorter, irregularly smooth or sometimes porose, angular cells coloured and inflated. Capsule very rare. — Tufts robust, on damp soil, usually in the alpine region.

Reported from **S.** *LL.—TL.* **N.** *STrd., Trs., Fnm.* **F.** *Le.* (North and Central Europe, Pyrenees, Asia, North America, Greenland).

This species is described by J. E. Zetterstedt from Luchons in the Pyrenees. No name has been so misused as *D. spadiceum*. In herbaria we could find most of our species of the genus *Dicranum* under this name. — In Botaniska Notiser, 1953, I have placed both *D. angustum* and *D. spadiceum* next to *D. groenlandicum*. Now, when I have seen the great variation of the genus *Dicranum* in mountain regions, I feel uncertain about these two species. I think the only way to understand them fully will be through cultivation experiments, together with studies in comparative anatomy.

28. Orthodicranum Loeske, Studien, 1910.

Dioicous. Leaves from lanceolate base longly and finely subulate, margin ± denticulate above; nerve $^1/_5$—$^1/_3$ the width of the leaf-base; cells in the upper part of the leaf quadrate to shortly rectangular, towards the base elongate ± porose, angular cells mostly unistratose, reaching nearly to the nerve. Capsule erect, smooth or slightly striate; peristome yellowish red, teeth divided to the middle or more. Spores 12—18 μ, ± papillose, mature in autumn.

I Leaves not obviously fragile; nerve ending in or below
   the apex, in cross section with stereids
   1 Cells in the upper part of the leaf mamillose, regularly
     quadrate or shortly rectangular, — fig. 31 B ....1. *O. montanum*
   2 Cells in the upper part of the leaf smooth, more irregular,
    — fig. 31 A ....2. *O. flagellare*
II Leaves fragile, nerve longly excurrent, in cross section
   without stereids ....3. *O. strictum*

1. O. montanum (Hedw.) Loeske, Studien, 1910; (*Dicranum montanum* Hedw., Sp. Musc., 1801). — Fig. 31 B.

Leaves soft, erect-spreading, slightly secund, strongly crisped when dry,

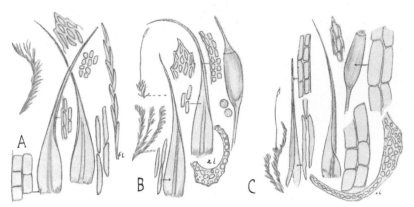

Fig. 31 A *Orthodicranum flagellare*,   fl. flagella,   B *O. montanum*,   C *O. strictum*.

the upper part of the margins and back of nerve denticulate; nerve in cross section with stereids; cells in the upper part of the leaf quadrate to shortly rectangular, regular, at back slightly mamillose, in lower part elongate, not or indistinctly porose, angular cells unistratose. Capsule erect or nearly so; annulus of 2 rows of large cells. Spores 14—18 μ, finely papillose, mature in summer. Vegetative propagation by means of small, lanceolate, easily detached leaves on short, clustered branches at the top of the main stems. — Soft green tufts, living chiefly on decaying wood, but also on rocks and sometimes on soil.

Common in forests from the lowlands to high in the mountains, but rarely above the forest line, **S. N. F.** throughout the territory. **D.** *Jl.*, *Sj.*, *Flst.*, *Brnh.* (Europe, Asia, North America).

The low, soft, compact, mostly light-green tufts are characteristic, as well as the dry, strongly crisped leaves which are mamillose at the back in the upper part and denticulate at margin. — For differences between this species and *Dicranoweisia cirrata* see under the latter.

2.   O. flagellare (Hedw.) Loeske, Studien, 1910; (*Dicranum flagellare* Hedw., Sp. Musc., 1801). — Fig. 31 A.

Leaves more or less secund, when dry slightly crisped, margin denticulate only near the apex; nerve with stereids; cells in upper part of leaf quadrate, rhomboid, irregular, smooth, towards the base elongate, incrassate, not or indistinctly porose, angular cells quadrate, unistratose. Capsule erect, annulus of 2 rows of large cells. Spores finely papillose, mature in autumn. Vegetative propagation by erect, flagelliform branches with small, appressed leaves from the axils of the upper stem-leaves — fig. 31 A, fl. — Tufts up to 5 cm high, bright or yellowish green, tomentose, occur chiefly on decaying wood, sometimes on soil.

Scattered in forests. **S.** *Sk.*—*Jmt.*, *Öl.*, *Gtl.* **N.** *ÖFld.*—*NTrd.* **F.** Southern and central parts to *Ks.* **D.** rare. *Jl.*, *Sj.* (Europe, Asia to China and Japan, North America).

3. O. strictum (Schleich.) Culm. in Bull. Soc. Bot. France, 1920; (*Dicranum strictum* Schleich., Crypt. Helv., 1806). — Fig. 31 C.

Leaves rigid, erect-spreading or slightly secund, not crisped when dry, from lanceolate base becoming subulate, apex fragile, often breaking off and taking root; nerve smooth, longly excurrent, in cross section without stereids; cells in the upper part of the leaf rectangular or quadrate, in the lower part elongate, more or less porose, angular cells inflated, hyaline or coloured, uni- or sparsely bistratose. Capsule erect or slightly curved; annulus not differentiated. Spores 14—18 μ, green, nearly smooth, mature in summer. — Compact, green, usually bright green tufts on decaying wood, seldom on soil.

Rare, but on Gtl. more widespread. **S.** *Sm., Vg., Upl., Öl., Gtl.,* **N.** *ÖAgd., Hdm., NTrd., Fnm.* **F.** *Al., Ab., Nyl., Ta., Sb.* **D.** rare *Jl., Brnh.* (West and Central Europe, Svalbard?, North America).

Sterile plants may be confused with *Dicranum fragilifolium*, but this species has a broader nerve, and the cells in the upper part of the leaf are shorter than those of O. *strictum*.

29. Metzlerella Hag. in K. N. V. Selsk. Skr., 1914.

Autoicous. Androecium bud-like, with a short stalk. Leaves narrowly lanceolate, subulate, erect-spreading or slightly secund; nerve broad and flattened, filling the greater part of the leaf. Capsule erect, narrowly ovate; peristome teeth divided towards the base into 2—3 prongs, at the apex closely and highly papillose, below with diagonal or vertical striae. Calyptra large, somewhat inflated. Stem with a wide central strand.

1. M. alpina (Schimp.) Hag. in K. N. V. Selsk. Skr., 1914; (*Metzleria alpina* Schimp., Milde, Br. Sil., 1869, *Metzleriella alpina* Limpr., Laubm., 1887). — Fig. 32.

Leaves with a long, fine, channelled subula, at apex entire or slightly denticulate; nerve broad; lamina narrow; cells linear at the margin, becoming wider towards the nerve and sometimes hyaline at the base. Capsule erect; lid rostrate; exothecial cells irregular, mostly elongate, incrassate; annulus and stomata lacking. Spores 20—24 μ, brown, finely papillose, mature in summer. — Tufts 1—2 cm high, blue-green, slightly glossy, with white or red tomentum below. Grows on damp humus, in rock crevices, in mountains up to 600 m.

Fig. 32. *Metzlerella alpina.*

Very rare. **N.** few localities in *Rog.* and *Hord.* (Alps).

30. Dicranodontium Br. Eur., 1847.

Dioicous. Androecium bud-like, at apex. Leaves narrow, channelled, longly and finely subulate, denticulate or serrulate; nerve broad, occupying the upper part of the leaf, in cross section with a median row of guide cells between two stereid bands; cells beside the nerve in lower part of the leaf inflated, elongate-hexagonal, becoming narrower above and towards the margins, angular cells reaching the nerve, mostly inflated and coloured, often fragile and vanishing. Seta curved, sometimes cygneous when moist, when dry erect or crooked; capsule smooth, cylindrical, regular; annulus and stomata lacking; lid rostrate; calyptra cucullate, entire or fringed at base; peristome below vertically striated, above with diagonal striae or papillose, teeth cleft to the base or nearly so. — Vegetative propagation by means of deciduous leaves.

I   Nerve below clearly delimited
   1 Nerve at back in the upper part of the leaf smooth or
     slightly mamillose, upper margin finely serrulate ....1. *D. uncinatum*
   2 Nerve at back in the upper part of the leaf highly mamil-
     lose, upper margin densely and sharply serrulate ....2. *D. asperulum*
II Nerve below indistinct ....3. *D. denudatum*

1.   D. uncinatum (Harv.) Jaeg., Ad. II, 1877—1878; (*Thysanomitrium unci-
    natum* Harv. in Hook., Ic. Pl., 1837; *Dicranum uncinatum* C. Müll.,
    Syn. Musc., 1849, *Dicranum circinatum* Wils., Br. Brit., 1855; *D. circi-
    natum* Schimp., Syn. Musc., 1876). — Fig. 33 A.

Leaves falcato-secund, longly subulate; margins finely serrulate to below the middle; nerve below distinct; cells beside the nerve in the lower part of the leaf inflated, hyaline, at margin narrower, above becoming rapidly linear, angular cells thin-walled, hyaline, soon destroyed. Seta about 1 cm, reddish; capsule elliptical; lid with a long beak; calyptra slightly fringed at base. — Tufts yellow-green, glossy, loose, up to 10 cm high on shaded damp or wet rocks, in mountains to 350 or 400 m.

Scattered localities on the coast. **N.** *Rog., Hord., SoFj.* (Great Britain, Central Europe).

Var. **subfalcatum** Limpr., Laubm., 1887; (*D. subfalcatum* Loeske et Osterw. in Bauer, Musci Eur. Exs.). — Fig. 33 a. — Leaves slightly falcato secund, near-ly erect; margins entire or slightly denticulate. The inflated basal cells become gradually narrowed above. Tufts dense, reddish below. On similar substrata as the type. — Very rare. **N.** *Rog., Hord.* (The Alps).

2.   D. asperulum Wils. in Kew Journ. Bot., 1857; (*Dicranum asperulum*
    Mitt. in Journ. Linn. Soc., Suppl., 1859; *D. aristatum* Schimp., Syn.
    Musc. Eur., 1860; *Didymodon aristatus* Lindb., Musci Scand., 1879).
    — Fig. 33 B.

Leaves erect-spreading or slightly secund, longly and finely subulate, deci-duous, margin densely and sharply serrulate throughout the whole length or nearly so; nerve at back in the upper part of the leaf closely and highly mamillose. Capsule brown; calyptra entire at base. — Tufts yellowish green or dull-green, on shaded, damp, siliceous rocks.

Rare but sometimes frequent on the coast. **N.** *Rog., Möre.* (West and Central Europe, Central Asia, North America).

Var. **falcatum** Milde in Bot. Zeit., 1870. Leaves secund, less serrulate. — **N.** *Hord.*

3.   D. denudatum (Brid.) E. G. Britton., N. Am. Fl., 1913; (*Dicranum
    denudatum* Brid., Musc. Rec. Suppl., 1806; *Didymodon longirostre*

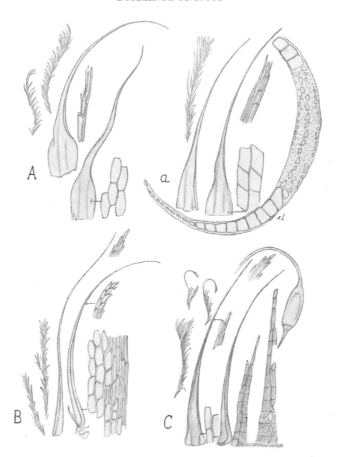

Fig. 33. A *Dicranodontium uncinatum*,   a var. *subfalcatum*,   B *D. asperulum*,
C *D. denudatum*.

Starke in Web. et Mohr, Bot. Taschenb., 1807; *D. longirostre*, Br. Eur.,
1848; *Didymodon denudatus* Lindb., Musci Scand. 1879). — Fig. 33 C.

Leaves erect-spreading or secund, longly and finely subulate, deciduous;
upper margin denticulate; nerve below indistinct, $^1/_2$ or $^1/_3$ the width of the
leaf at base; cells in the upper part of the leaf elongate, lower lamina cells
beside the nerve somewhat inflated, angular cells large, thin-walled, brown
or hyaline, often projecting from the lamina, auriculate. Seta yellow, cygneous;
capsule oblong, pale brown. Spores about 13 μ, slightly papillose, mature in
autumn. — Tufts green or yellowish green, soft, with red-brown tomentum;
on shaded damp rocks, humus or decaying wood.

Scattered in the western provinces, rare in the East. **S.** *Sk.*—*Hjd.* **N.** *Busk.*—
—*Nrdl.* **F.** *Nyl.* (Europe, Asia to Japan, North America).

Var. **alpinum** (Schimp.) Hag.; (*Campylopus alpinus* Schimp.). Leaves rigid, nearly erect, entire, not deciduous. — **N.** acc. to Hagen, confined to the Vestland.

D. denudatum is recognized by the nerve which is indistinct below, and the wide auricles.

31. Campylopus Brid., Musc. Rec. Suppl., 1819.

Dioicous, generally sterile. Leaves from lanceolate base more or less longly subulate, apex channelled or tubular, slightly denticulate or entire; nerve broad, usually excurrent; lamina narrow, cells largest beside the nerve, narrowed towards the margins, angular cells more or less differentiated, reaching the nerve, often auriculate. Seta arcuate to cygneous when moist, curved to erect when dry; capsule generally striate, sulcate when dry, elliptical, symmetrical or slightly curved; annulus of 2—3 rows of large cells, separating; stomata lacking; peristome cleft to the middle, below vertically pointstriated, above papillose; calyptra cucullate, mostly fringed at base. Vegetative propagation usually by means of fragile buds or branches. — A large genus consisting of c. 500 species with a geographical distribution principally in the tropics, Central America, and Africa.

I　Nerve with stereids
　　1 Stereid bands on dorsal and ventral surface of nerve;
　　　　— fig. 34 A, xn ....1. *C. brevipilus*
　　2 Stereid band only on the dorsal side of the nerve; —
　　　　fig. 34 E, xl
　　　　a Cells in upper part of lamina chiefly rectangular;
　　　　　leaves without hyaline point
　　　　　b Lamina broadest below; — fig. 34 B and C
　　　　　　c Nerve excurrent, angular cells indistinct ....2. *C. piriformis*
　　　　　　cc Nerve percurrent; angular cells inflated, well
　　　　　　　differentiated ....3. *C. flexuosus*
　　　　　bb Lamina contracted at base; — fig. 34 D................4. *C. fragilis*
　　　　aa Cells in upper lamina narrowly rhomboid, vermi-
　　　　　cular; leaves with long hyaline point ....5. *C. atrovirens*
II　Nerve without stereids
　　　　a Robust species; lamina short, not reaching above the
　　　　　lower half of the leaf; angular cells inflated, well
　　　　　differentiated ....6. *C. schwarzii*
　　　　aa Smaller species; lamina reaching above the middle
　　　　　of the leaf; angular cells not or only slightly differen-
　　　　　tiated.
　　　　　b Nerve at back furrowed with projecting cells; — fig.
　　　　　　34 G, xl; — tufts loose, radiculose only at base..........7. *C. subulatus*
　　　　　bb Nerve smooth at back; — tufts compact, matted
　　　　　　with rufous tomentum ....8. *C. schimperi*

1. C. brevipilus Br. Eur., 1847. — Fig. 34 A.

Leaves erecto-patent, from lanceolate, somewhat ovate base becoming subulate, with a short, toothed, hyaline point, margin recurved above; nerve about ⅓ the width of the base, ending below the apex or percurrent; angular cells more or less differentiated, brownish or hyaline — above this, cells beside the nerve rectangular, quadrate, towards margins several rows of linear, hyaline cells — upper cells prosenchymatous, vermicular. Plants with capsule very rare. — Tufts 1—3, seldom up to 10 cm high, green, yellowish green or yellow-brown, dense but not tomentose; on damp soil.

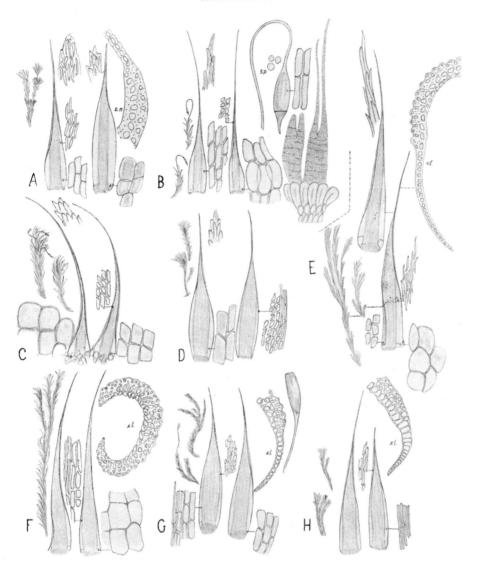

Fig. 34 A *Campylopus brevipilus*, B *C. piriformis*, C *C. flexuosus*, D *C. fragilis*, E *C. atrovirens*, F *C. schwarzii*, G *C. subulatus*, H *C. schimperi*.

Rare. **N.** *Rog.*—*STrd.* near the sea. **D.** *Jl.*, *Fy.* (West Europe, Switzerland, Azores, Madeira, Algeria).

Because the leaves are crowded at the top of the annual stem-growth, older plants usually have a nodose appearance. The vermicular cells of the upper part of the lamina are characteristic of this species and *C. atrovirens*.

2. C piriformis (Schultz) Brid., Br. Univ., 1826; (*Dicranum piriforme* Schultz, Fl. Star. Suppl., 1819; *Dicranum turfaceum* C. Müll., Syn. Musc. I, 1849; *C. turfaceus*, Br. Eur., 1849). — Fig. 34 B.

Leaves erecto-patent, slightly flexuose, from lanceolate base, longly and finely subulate; nerve $^1/_2 - ^2/_5$ the width of the base, excurrent in a short, usually green, denticulate point; angular cells slightly differentiated; cells at base of leaf beside the nerve rectangular, thin-walled, more or less hyaline; at the margin several rows of linear cells; apical cells small, quadrate, shortly rhomboid or rectangular. Seta yellow, capsule elliptical, olive-green, furrowed. Spores about 12 μ, sparsely and finely papillose, mature in spring. Vegetative propagation by means of buds with small closely overlapping leaves. — Tufts 1—4 cm high, yellowish green, only slightly tomentose at base; occurs on peaty moorlands, on the side of ditches, etc.

Scattered localities. **S.** *Sk., Bl., Hl., Öl.* **N.** *ÖFld., Rog., SoFj.* **D.** not uncommon. (Europe, Azores, Yenisei).

For the difference between *C. piriformis* and *C. flexuosus* see the note under the latter species.

3. C. flexuosus (Hedw.) Brid., Mant. Musc., 1819; (*Dicranum flexuosum* Hedw., Sp. Musc., 1801). — Fig. 34 C.

Leaves erecto-patent or often slightly secund, from lanceolate base, subulate, denticulate at point; nerve $^1/_2$ the width of the base, percurrent; angular cells inflated, often forming a well-differentiated auricular group; immediately above are rectangular cells, inflated beside nerve, narrowed towards margins; apical cells small, quadrate, rectangular, rhomboidal, in rather regular rows. Capsule elliptical, furrowed, often slightly asymmetrical. Spores about 12 μ, sparsely and finely papillose, mature in spring. Vegetative propagation by means of short apical branches with small leaves. — Tufts dense, green to yellowish green, 1—6 cm high, below tomentose with brownish red radicles; occurs on damp peat, shaded humus-covered rocks, in crevices, etc.

Scattered localities. **S.** *Sk., Bl.* and in the west provinces *Hl.—Dsl.* **N.** Common in the Vestland, *ÖAgd., NTrd.* **D.** *Jl., Fy., Sj., Brnh.* (Europe, Azores, Madeira, Canaries).

C. flexuosus is usually more robust and more tomentose than *C. piriformis*. A comparison between cross sections of the nerve of these species shows a difference in cell number: the majority of the ventral cells of *C. flexuosus* are divided so that there are two ventral cells above every guide cell. In *C. piriformis* the guide and ventral cells are arranged alternately. The two species are closely related. Some authors regard them as forms of the same species.

4. C. fragilis (Turn.) Br. Eur., 1848; (*Dicranum flexuosum* β *fragile* Turn., Musc. Hib., 1804; *Dicranum densum* Schleich., Exs. et Cat., 1807; *Dicranum Schleicheri* C. Müll., Syn. Musc. 1, 1849). — Fig. 34 D.

Leaves erecto-patent, from ovate base, finely subulate; lamina narrow, contracted at base; nerve $^1/_2 - ^1/_3$ the width of the base, shortly excurrent; angular cells hardly differentiated; basal cells large, thin-walled, somewhat inflated, and hyaline, gradually becoming rectangular with thick transverse and thin longitudinal walls; apical cells small, rhomboid; marginal cells linear. Capsule like those of the preceding species. Vegetative propagation by means of numerous small branches between the apical leaves. — Tufts green to yellowish green, 1—3 cm high, compact, radiculose; occurs on lime-free rocks, rock crevices, seldom on peaty or sandy ground.

Rather common in the Vestland of Norway, elsewhere rare. **S.** *Sk?, Hl., Vg., Boh.* **N.** *ÖAgd.* — *Möre.* **D.** *Flst., Sj.* (Europe, Azores, Madeira).

The densely leaved stem apex, the pencil-like habit, and the shining white leaf bases are characteristic of this species.

5.   C. atrovirens DNot., Syll. Musc., 1838; (*Dicranum flexuosum* γ *piliferum* Turn., Musc. Hib., 1804). — Fig. 34 E.

Leaves erecto-patent or slightly secund, from lanceolate base, longly and finely subulate; nerve about $^1/_2$ the width of the leaf, excurrent in a long, denticulate hyaline subula; angular cells thin-walled, strongly inflated, brown or red-brown or hyaline, forming well differentiated auricles; other cells incrassate, those of the base shortly rectangular, quadrate, vermicular above. Capsule very rare. Vegetative propagation by means of fragile apical shoots. — Tufts usually robust, glossy green or brown-green to blackish; on damp rocks, peaty soils, etc.

Common in the Vestland of Norway, elsewhere rare. **S.** *Vg.* **N.** *Rog.—NTrd., Opl.* (West to South Europe, Alps, North America).

6.   C. schwarzii Schimp., Br. Eur. Suppl., 1864. — Fig. 34 F.

Leaves erecto-patent, slightly secund, longly and finely subulate; lamina short and narrow, not reaching the middle of the leaf; nerve $^2/_3$ the width of the base, excurrent in a long, green, gradually narrowed subula, entire or with few teeth; angular cells inflated, hyaline or reddish, forming a small projecting group; lamina cells thin-walled, linear at margins, shorter and broader beside the nerve. Vegetative propagation by means of fragile apical shoots. — Tufts robust, glossy, green to brownish green; occurs on damp rocks, peaty soils, etc.

Rather common in the Vestland of Norway. **N.** *VAgd.—Möre.* (West Europe, Alps, Bukovina).

7.   C. subulatus Milde in Bot. Zeit., 1862; (*C. brevifolius* Schimp., Br. Eur. Suppl., 1864; *Orthopus brevifolius* Wulfsb. in K. N. V. Selsk. Skr., 1875). — Fig. 34 G.

Leaves rigid, erecto-patent, from lanceolate base, shortly subulate; lamina narrow, at the apex reduced to a single row of cells; nerve about $^2/_3$ the width of the base, narrowed into a short, excurrent point, entire or with few teeth, sometimes hyaline; angular cells hardly differentiated, basal cells beside the nerve rectangular, thin-walled, hyaline; at margin some rows of linear, colourless cells extending upwards from base; apical cells small, thick-walled, rectangular, quadrate or rhomboid. Capsule elliptical, nearly smooth, rare. Vegetative propagation by means of fragile, apical shoots. — In loose slender tufts, 1—2 cm high, green to yellowish green; on sandy banks, siliceous rocks, etc.

Rather common in the Vestland of Norway, elsewhere rare. **S.** *Dsl., Vg.* **N.** *Rog.—Möre.* (West Europe, Alps).

8. C. schimperi Milde in Bot. Zeit., 1864. — Fig. 34 H.

Leaves erecto-patent with a long or short subula; lamina narrow, reaching towards the apex; angular cells few, inflated, hyaline or reddish, fragile; above this beside the nerve a few rectangular, somewhat inflated cells, becoming linear, colourless at the margin; apical cells small, thick-walled, rectangular or rhomboid. Capsule not known from Scandinavia. Vegetative propagation by means of fragile apical shoots or by small flagella-like branches. — Tufts green to yellowish green, 1—3, seldom up to 6 cm high, compact and radiculose; on stones and soil from sea-level to 1400 m in mountains.

Scattered localities near the sea and in the mountains inland. **N.** *Rog.—Trs.* (West Europe from Iceland to the Pyrenees, Central Europe, Caucasus, North America).

32. Paraleucobryum (Lindb.) Loeske in Hedwigia, 1908; (Lindb., Musci Scand., 1879 as sect. of *Dicranum*).

Dioicous. Leaves lanceolate-subulate; nerve broad, sometimes occupying the whole upper part of the leaf, in cross section the nerve is composed of 3—4 layers of cells: a chlorophyllose middle layer surrounded on both sides by a layer of more or less hyaline cells. *P. sauteri* and *P. longifolium* have in addition ridges of mamillose, projecting, chlorophyllose cells at back of nerve. Stereids lacking. Cells above rectangular, below elongate, slightly porose, — angular cells well differentiated, inflated, brownish or hyaline. Capsule erect, cylindrical, straight or slightly incurved; stomata in two rows; peristome like that of *Dicranum*; lid rostrate. Spores papillose, mature in summer. — *Dicranum*-like mosses occurring in woods or in mountains on tree trunks, soil, and rocks. Bright green when moist, ± albescent when dry.

I   Nerve less than ½ the width of leaf base ....4. *P. sauteri*
II Nerve ½ or more the width of leaf base
    1 Leaf margin serrulate; nerve rough at back ....2. *P. longifolium*
    2 Leaf margin smooth or with a few teeth at apex; nerve
      smooth ....3. *P. enerve*

1. P. sauteri (Br. Eur.) Loeske in Hedwigia, 1908; (*Dicranum Sauteri* Br. Eur., 1847; *P. longifolium* ssp. *Sauteri* C. Jens., Skand. Bladmossfl., 1939). — Fig. 35 A.

Leaves slightly secund, somewhat rigid, longly subulate; margin with small, scattered teeth or nearly entire; nerve $^1/_3$—$^1/_5$ the width of the leaf; cells above rectangular, below elongate, slightly porose. Capsule erect. — Bright green tufts on tree trunks or soil, seldom on rocks.

Rare. **S.** *Vg., PL.* **N.** *Opl., Möre., STrd., Nrdl.* (The mountains of Central Europe, South Europe, Caucasus, Siberia, Japan).

Closely related to the following species and often called a variety or ssp. of this. *P. sauteri* occurs on soil, *P. longifolium* on stones. *P. sauteri* has shorter leaves, less rough above; the nerve is smaller.

2. P. longifolium (Hedw.) Loeske in Hedwigia, 1908; (*Dicranum longifolium* Hedw., Sp. Musc., 1801). — Fig. 35 B.

Leaves mostly secund, longly and finely subulate; margin distinctly denticulate; nerve broad, $^1/_2$ or more the width of the base, occupying the upper

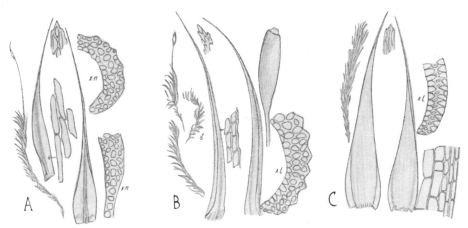

Fig. 35 A *Paraleucobryum sauteri*, from spec. of Central Europe, B *P. longifolium*, C *P. enerve*.

part of the leaf; cells above rectangular, below elongate, slightly porose, angular cells inflated, hyaline or brownish. Capsule nearly erect; annulus lacking. — Somewhat silky-glossy, light to dark green tufts on siliceous stones, seldom on tree trunks.

Common in wood region but sparse towards North, rare in mountains. **S. N. F. D.** spread over the whole territory. (Europe, Asia, North America, Greenland).

An alpine form is var. **strictiforme** (C. Jens.) Broth., Laubm. Fennosk., 1923, (*Dicranum longifolium* β *strictiforme* C. Jens., Medd. Grönl., 1887). Leaves rigid, nearly straight, shorter and less denticulate above. Tufts dense, dark green. — Is known from **S.**, *LL.*, *TL.* **F.** *Li.* (Greenland) — var. *subalpinum* Milde in the Alps and North America is perhaps the same form.

3. P. enerve (Thed.) Loeske in Hedwigia, 1908; (*Dicranum enerve* Thed., Hartm., Skand. Fl., 1849; *Dicranum albicans* Br. Eur., 1850). — Fig. 35 C.

Leaves erecto-patent to nearly erect, sometimes slightly secund; margin entire or with few teeth at apex; nerve smooth, very broad, occupying the greater part of the leaf, only below is there a narrow lamina. Capsule erect with a separating annulus. — In dense, whitish green, silky tufts; on siliceous soil and rocks in mountains, mostly above the tree limit.

Often frequent at high altitudes. **S.** *Hjd.*—*TL.* **N.** *ÖAgd.*—*Nrdl.* **F.** *Le.* (Europe, Caucasus, Sikkim, Japan, North America).

33. **Leucobryum** Hampe in Flora, 1837.

Leaves erecto-patent or secund, lanceolate, more or less tubular in the upper part; nerve very broad, in cross section one layer of 4-sided chlorocysts, — fig. 36 a — surrounded by 1—4 layers of leucocysts, — fig. 36 b. — Seta long; capsule curved, striated and strumose. Plants in dense, albescent or glaucous cushions.

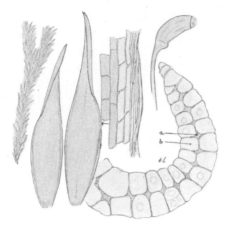

Fig. 36 *Leucobryum glaucum.*

1. L. glaucum (Hedw.) Schimp., Br. Eur. Coroll., 1855; (*Dicranum glaucum* Hedw., Sp. Musc., 1801). — Fig. 36.

Dioicous. Leaves crowded, from ovate-lanceolate base gradually narrowed, cuspidate; margin in upper part incurved, entire or slightly denticulate at apex; nerve broad, occupying greater part of leaf, in cross section with 1—4 layers of leucocysts; lamina forms a narrow band from the base of the leaf up towards the apex; cells hyaline, narrow-elongate at margins, rectangular beside the nerve. Sporophyte very rare; capsule brown, curved, with 8 darker striae; peristome brown-red, vertically point-striated below, papillose above. Spores 14—18 µ, yellowish, slightly papillose, mature in autumn. — Albescent or glaucous, compact cushions on damp soils or slopes in woods, on heaths, etc.

Common in wooded districts: **S.** *Sk.—Dlr., Öl., Gtl.* **N.** *ÖFld.—Nrdl.* **F.** *Al., Ab., Nyl., Ta., Ka.* **D.** spread over the whole territory. (Europe, Azores, Canaries, Madeira, Caucasus, Japan, North America).

Order 3. **Pottiales**

Leaves linear to broadly ovate-lanceolate, often papillose in the upper part. Peristome single or lacking, teeth 16. Acrocarpous.

Fam. VI. **Encalyptaceae**

Autoicous, seldom dioicous. Perigonium mostly lateral just below the perichaetium. Leaves broadly linear, lingulate or spathulate, margin mostly plane, rarely revolute, lamina flat or incurved, when dry crisped or incurved and twisted; nerve broad, ending below the apex or excurrent into a ± long point, at back strongly prominent, in cross section large inner cells surrounded by smaller cells, — fig. 37 F, xn; — cells in upper part of leaf quadrate, hexagonal, chlorophyllose, densely papillose, — in basal part of leaf cells rectangular, wide, hyaline, often rufous or brownish, fragile, — at margin several rows of linear cells constitute a ± distinct border. Seta erect, crisped when dry; capsule cylindrical, erect, smooth or striated, usually furrowed when dry and empty; peristome lacking, single or double, when present teeth reddish and papillose with or without preperistome; calyptra large, cylindrical, covering the whole capsule or nearly so, at base erose, lacerated or fringed; lid long-beaked, falling off with the calyptra. Spores usually large, papillose, wrinkled, or smooth. — Central strand of stem slightly developed.

The family is characterized by the lingulate or spathulate, in the upper part strongly papillose leaves, the large tubular calyptra and the erect cylindrical capsule.

34. Encalypta Hedw., Sp. Musc., 1801.
With characteristics of the family.

1. E. streptocarpa Hedw., Sp. Musc., 1801; (*E. contorta* Lindb. in Öfv. K. V. A. Förh., 1863; *Leersia contorta* Lindb., Musci Scand., 1879). — Fig. 37 A.

Dioicous. Leaves lingulate to spathulate, obtuse, strongly crisped when dry; nerve ending below the apex, never excurrent; cells at margin in the basal part of the leaf linear, constituting a slightly denticulate, yellowish border. Seta reddish, rough; capsule striated, spirally furrowed when dry; peristome double; calyptra fringed at base. Spores 8—12 μ, yellowish green, smooth, mature in summer. Vegetative propagation by means of jointed protonematal threads formed in the axils of the upper leaves, (fig. 37 A, gt). — Our most robust species, tufts up to 5 cm high, loose or compact, on soil or rocks preferably in calcareous districts, from the lowlands to the low-alpine region.

Rather common in suitable localities, capsule very rare. **S. N. F. D.** in most provinces. (Europe, the Canaries, Asia, North America).

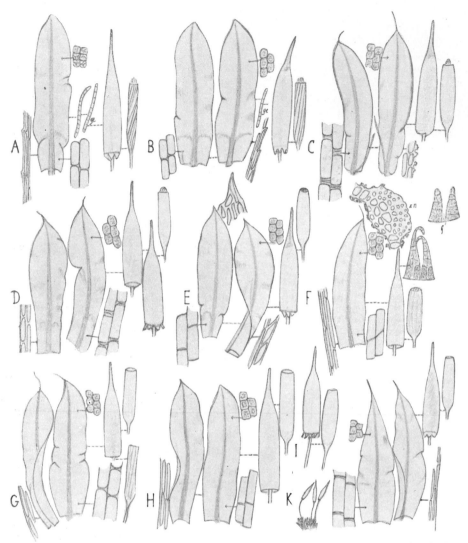

Fig. 37. A *Encalypta streptocarpa*, B *E. procera*, C *E. affinis*, D *E. brevicolla*,
E *E. ciliata*, F *E. rhabdocarpa*, f var. *leptodon*, G *E. spathulata*, H *E. vulgaris*,
I *E. mutica*, K *E. alpina*.

2. **E. procera** Bruch in Deutsch. Akad. Münch., 1828; (*Leersia procera*
    Lindb., Musci Scand., 1879; *E. cucullata* C. Müll. et Kindb. in Macoun,
    Cat. Can., 1892). — Fig. 37 B.

Closely related to the preceding species but autoicous and usually with
fruit. Leaves like those of *E. streptocarpa* but the nerve sometimes excurrent
in a ± long point. Capsule striated, with slightly spiral furrows when dry;
seta smooth. Spores larger than those of the preceding species, about 18—20 μ,

slightly papillose or nearly smooth. Stem with central strand (in *E. strepto-carpa* the central strand is absent or very slightly developed). Vegetative propagation = the preceding species. — Usually less robust than *E. strepto-carpa*, occurring in similar habitats but restricted to mountain districts.

Scattered localities. **S.** *Hjd., Jmt., PL., LL., TL.* **N.** *Opl.,°Hdm., STrd.—Fnm.* **F.** *Kl?, Ks.* (North Europe, Siberia, North America).

3. E. affinis Hedw. fil. in Web. et Mohr, Beitr. zur Naturk., 1805; (*E. apophysata* Nees. et Hornsch., Br. Germ., 1827; *Leersia affinis* Lindb., Musci Scand., 1879). — Fig. 37 C.

Leaves narrowly lingulate to spathulate, margin revolute in the middle of the leaf; nerve ending below the apex or excurrent, in the upper leaves usually ending in a hyaline hair; the basal cells with scattered tall, simple or forked papillae, — the transverse walls brown, strongly thickened, — longitudinal walls thin, border indistinct. Seta reddish; capsule smooth; peristome double; calyptra fringed at base. Spores 20—30 µ, finely papillose, mature in summer. — In wide tufts on soil or in rock-crevices, preferably in calcareous districts in the mountain region.

Scattered localities. **S.** *Hjd., LyL., PL., LL., TL.* **N.** *Akh., Busk., STrd., Nrdl., Trs., Fnm.* **F.** *Kl., Kb., Ks., Le., Lps.* (Europe, Asia, North America).

Sterile specimens easily recognized by the brown, strongly thickened, transverse walls of the basal cells and the tall, simple or forked papillae scattered at base of leaf.

4. E. brevicolla Bruch in sched., Unio Itin., 1829; (*E. longicolla* β *brevicolla* Br. Eur., 1838; *Leersia brevicolla* Lindb., Musci Scand., 1879). — Fig. 37 D.

Leaves lingulate to spathulate, margin plane, upper leaves usually with a longer or shorter hyaline hair point; the basal cells smooth or sparsely and indistinctly papillose, transverse walls strongly thickened, brown, the longitudinal narrow border more or less distinct. Seta reddish; capsule smooth, calyptra fringed at base. Spores 30—40 µ, coarsely papillose. — Tufts loose or dense, 0,5—2 cm high on dry soil or in rock crevices, preferably in calcareous districts, from the lowlands to the mountains.

Scattered localities. **S.** *Vrm., Upl., Dlr., Hls., Mpd., Hjd.—TL.* **N.** *ÖAgd.—Fnm.* **F.** *Al., Ta., Sa., Kl., Tb., Sb., Kb., Ob., Ok.* — *Lps.* (Reported from Labrador and the East Coast of Greenland).

Like the preceding species but the base of the leaf is smooth or with a few low papillae. The spores are coarsely papillose. (*E. affinis* has finely papillose spores).

5. E. ciliata Hedw., Sp. Musc., 1801; (*Leersia laciniata* Lindb. in Acta Soc. Sc. Fenn., 1872; ?*E. Macounii* Aust. in Bot. Gaz., 1877; ?*Leersia borealis* Kindb., Laubm. Schw. Norw., 1883). — Fig. 37 E.

Leaves lingulate to spathulate; nerve ending just below the apex or shortly excurrent; the wide basal cells thin-walled, without papillae, border more or less distinct. Seta yellow, or when older reddish; capsule smooth; peristome simple, preperistome present or absent; calyptra fringed at base. Spores 30—35 µ, wrinkled or smooth, mature in summer. — Tufts 1—3 cm high, loose or dense, on shaded, calcareous or non-calcareous soil, in rock crevices, etc. from lowlands to mountains.

Scattered localities. **S. N. F.** in most provinces. (Europe, Algeria, the mountains of Central Africa, Abyssinia, Asia to Japan and Formosa).

This plant is known by the simple peristome, the calyptra strongly fringed at base, and the characteristic wrinkled spores.

6. **E. rhabdocarpa** Schwaegr., Suppl. I., 1811; (*Leersia rhabdocarpa* Lindb., Musci Scand., 1879; *E. leiomitra* Kindb. in Macoun, Cat. Can. Pl., 1892). — Fig. 37 F.

Leaves narrowly lingulate to spathulate, at apex somewhat incurved; margin plane; nerve ending just below the apex or excurrent in a ± long, hyaline hair point; cells in upper part of the leaf about 15—16 μ; the wide basal cells mostly thin-walled, at margin becoming linear, incrassate, yellowish, constituting a more or less distinct border. Seta red; capsule striated; peristome simple, teeth red or yellowish, preperistome prominent or lacking. Spores 35—50 μ, brownish, with dense, large, warty papillae, mature in summer. — In wide, dense tufts or mats, on soil or rocks in calcareous districts from the lowlands to high in the mountains.

Scattered localities in the lowlands, common in mountains. **S.** *Boh., Vg., Ög., Upl., Vstm., Dlr.—TL., Öl., Gtl.* **N. F.** most provinces. **D.** *Jl.* (Europe, Asia, North America, Hawaii).

Var. **leptodon** (Br. Eur.) Lindb. — Fig. 37 F, f. — The striae of the capsule are weaker than those of the type, the peristome is paler and less developed, preperistome absent. Occurs here and there within the area. — Var. **nuda** Hag. Peristome absent, leaves apiculate, not piliferous. — Recorded by Hagen from a few localities in Norway.

E. rhabdocarpa is known by the red seta, furrowed capsule, calyptra erose at base, and the spores covered with tall, warty papillae.

7. **E. spathulata** C. Müll., Syn I., 1849; (*Leersia spathulata* Lindb., Musci Scand., 1879; *E. rhabdocarpa* var. *spathulata* Hag. in K. N. V. Selsk. Skr., 1910). — Fig. 37 G.

Leaves narrowly lingulate, spathulate; nerve in the upper leaves excurrent in a hyaline hair point; cells in upper part of the leaf 11—12 μ, those at the margin forming a yellowish border of linear cells. Capsule slightly striated, when dry somewhat spirally furrowed; calyptra erose at base. Spores 30—40 μ, papillose. — In dense tufts on ± calcareous soil.

Rare, in scattered localities. **S.** *Ög., Dlr., Hjd.* **N.** *Akh., Tel., Rog.—Nrdl.* **F.** *Kl.* (Central Europe)

Can be confused with *E. rhabdocarpa* without peristome. However *E. spathulata* has smaller cells, 11—12 μ, in the upper part of the leaf.

8. **E. vulgaris** Hedw., Sp. Musc., 1801; *E. extinctoria* Sw., 1799, Hartm., Skand. Fl., 1871). — Fig. 37 H.

Leaves narrowly lingulate or spathulate, obtuse or shortly acute, at apex somewhat incurved; nerve ending below the apex, sometimes excurrent in a short point, rarely in a ± long hair point; cells in the upper part of the leaf 12—16 μ, basal cells hyaline, older leaves with brownish walls; at margins cells narrowed and constituting a more or less distinct yellowish border.

Capsule when moist smooth, when dry and empty furrowed; calyptra erose at base. Spores 30—40 μ, with large, rounded papillae, mature in spring. — In wide tufts on more or less calcareous soil, on earth-covered stone-walls, etc. in the lowlands.

Common in the southern provinces, otherwise scattered or rare. **S.** *Sk.—Dlr., Gstr., Mpd., Öl., Gtl.* **N.** in the south part to *Busk.* **F.** *Al., Ab., Nyl., Ka., Ta.* **D.** the whole country. (Europe, Canaries, Madeira, North Africa, Asia, New Guinea, New Zealand, North America).

This species is characterized by the smooth capsule and the calyptra entire or erose at base. Leaves usually obtuse but variable. — Forma **obtusa** (Br. Germ.) C. Jens. Leaf apex obtuse; nerve ending far below the apex. — Forma **apiculata** Br. Germ. Nerve excurrent and ending in a short point. — Forma **pilifera** (Lindb.) C. Jens. Nerve ending in a ± long hair point.

9. E. mutica Hag. in Tromsö Mus. Aarsh., 1899. — Fig. 37 I.

Leaves resembling those of the preceding species, but the point is always obtuse; the nerve is thinner, ceasing far below the apex, never excurrent; border at the base absent or slightly developed. Capsule cylindrical, smooth; calyptra fringed below. Spores rather finely papillose. — Low dense tufts on bare soil and rocks.

Rare. **S.** *Vg., Nb.?* **N.** *Busk., Opl., STrd., Nrdl., Fnm.* **F.** *Ks., Le.*

This species is confined to Fennoscandia. It is characterized by the fringed calyptra, the capsule without peristome, rather finely papillose spores, and the leaf with the nerve ending far below the apex.

10. E. alpina Sm., Engl. Bot., 1805; (*E. commutata* Br. Germ., 1827; *Leersia alpina* Lindb., Musci Scand., 1879). — Fig. 37 K.

Leaves oblong-lanceolate, gradually narrowed; nerve excurrent in a ± long, sharp point; cells in the upper part of the leaf small, about 10 μ, obscure, densely papillose, towards the base elongate, rectangular, hyaline, at margin some rows of linear cells constituting a distinct border. Capsule smooth; peristome absent; calyptra fringed at base. Spores about 30—35 μ, finely papillose. — In low, dense tufts on calcareous soil or rocks.

Common in the mountains. **S.** *Hjd.—TL.* **N.** *Hord.—Trs., Fnm.* **F.** *Ks., Le.* (Europe, Morocco, Asia, North America).

Recognized by the leaves which are gradually narrowed from the middle to an acute point, and the small opaque cells in the upper part of the leaves. The capsule is smooth without a peristome and the calyptra is fringed.

Abbreviations of geographical names

S = Sweden   **N** = Norway   **F** = Finland   **D** = Denmark   **R** = Russia

Ab	= Regio aboënsis		*Mpd*	= Medelpad
Akh	= Akershus		*Mö*	= Möen
Al	= Alandia		*Möre*	= Möre
Bl	= Blekinge		*Nb*	= Norrbotten
Boh	= Bohuslän		*Nrdl*	= Nordland
Brnh	= Bornholm		*Nrk*	= Närke
Busk	= Buskerud		*NTrd*	= Nord-Tröndelag
Dlr	= Dalarna (Dalecarlia)		*Nyl*	= Nylandia
Dsl	= Dalsland		*Oa*	= Ostrobottnia australis
Flst	= Falster		*Ob*	= Ostrobottnia borealis
Fnm	= Finmark		*Ok*	= Ostrobottnia kajanensis
Fy	= Fyen		*Ol*	= Karelia olonetsensis
Gbg	= District of Göteborg (parts		*Om*	= Ostrobottnia media
	of Bohuslän and Väster-		*On*	= Karelia onegensis
	götland)		*Opl*	= Opland
Gstr	= Gästrikland		*PL*	= Pite Lappmark
Gtl	= Gotland		*Rog*	= Rogaland
Hdm	= Hedmark		*Sa*	= Savonia australis
Hjd	= Härjedalen		*Sb*	= Savonia borealis
Hl	= Halland		*Sj*	= Själland
Hls	= Hälsingland		*Sk*	= Skåne (Scania)
Hord	= Hordaland		*Sm*	= Småland
Ik	= Isthmus karelicus		*SoFj*	= Sogn og Fjordane
Im	= Lapponia Imandrae		*Srm*	= Södermanland
Jl	= Jylland (Jutland)		*St*	= Satakunta
Jmt	= Jämtland		*STrd*	= Sör-Tröndelag
Ka	= Karelia australis		*Ta*	= Tavastia australis
Kb	= Karelia borealis		*Tb*	= Tavastia borealis
Kk	= Karelia keretina		*Tel*	= Telemark
Kl	= Karelia ladogensis		*TL*	= Torne Lappmark
Kp	= Karelia pomorica		*Trs*	= Troms
Ks	= Kuusamo		*Upl*	= Uppland
Langel	= Langeland		*VAgd*	= Vest-Agder
Le	= Lapponia enontekiensis		*Vb*	= Västerbotten
Li	= Lapponia inarensis		*VFld*	= Vestfold
Lk	= Lapponia kemensis		*Vg*	= Västergötland
LL	= Lule Lappmark		*Vrm*	= Värmland
Lmur	= Lapponia murmanica		*Vstm*	= Västmanland
Loll	= Lolland		*Äng*	= Ångermanland
Lp	= Lapponia ponojensis		*ÄsL*	= Åsele Lappmark
Lps	= Lapponia petsamoënsis		*ÖAgd*	= Öst-Agder
Lt	= Lapponia tulomensis		*ÖFld*	= Östfold
Lv	= Lapponia Varsugae		*Ög*	= Östergötland
LyL	= Lycksele Lappmark		*Öl*	= Öland

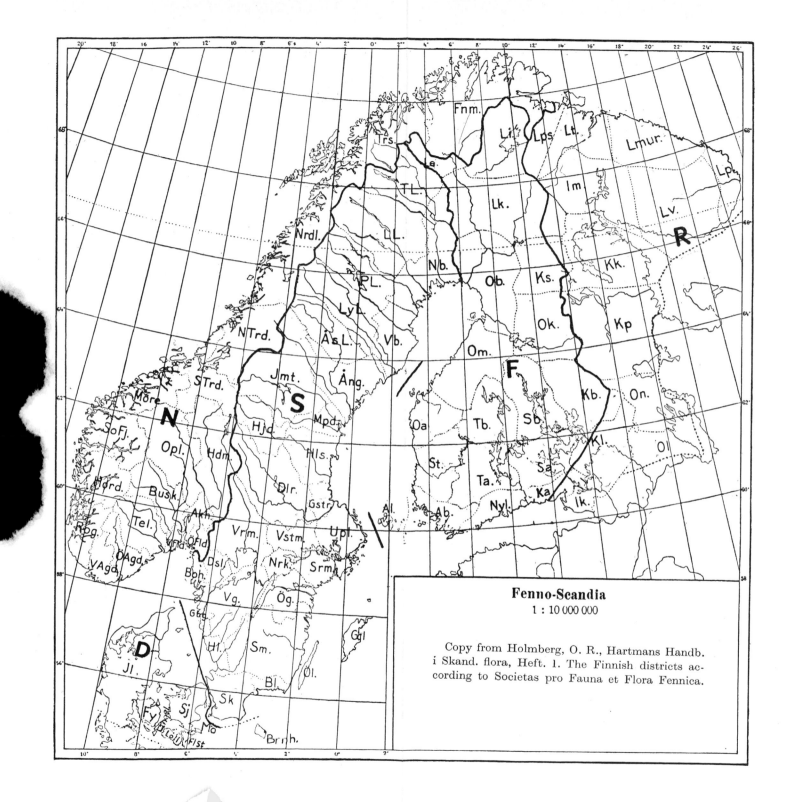

Fenno-Scandia

1 : 10 000 000

Copy from Holmberg, O. R., Hartmans Handb.
i Skand. flora, Heft. 1. The Finnish districts according to Societas pro Fauna et Flora Fennica.